Nurse

Nurse

a memoir

Rachel E. Ostrander, RN, MSN, ARNP

REO Writes

First Printing, 2022
Second Printing, 2023

Cover Photograph: Hush Naidoo Jade Photography on Unsplash
Author Photograph: Jonathon Alexander

Identifiers:
ISBN (paperback) 979-8-9862112-0-6
ISBN (EPUB) 979-8-9-9862112-1-3

Library of Congress Control Number: 2022908533

These stories have been adapted to protect the privacy of the many people who shared moments of their lives with me. Consider them to be fictionalized reality.

Name, age, gender, place, medical diagnosis, and other identifying details have been changed to protect the people written into this book. Any actual reproduction of someone's life is purely coincidental.

Trigger warning. Some of these stories contain content about death, dying, end of life, hospice, suicide, drug abuse, shame, or trauma.

CONTENTS

CONTENTS

CONTENTS

Blooming

CONTENTS

For those who care for others.

You show up.
You make a difference.
You make the world better.

This book is for you.
Thank you.

Introduction

66

Let us never consider ourselves finished nurses.
We must be learning all of our lives.

- Florence Nightingale

Wilt (Part 1).

I frequently see a pleasant seventy-year-old man in the clinic where I work as a nurse practitioner. He carries a large paper calendar and writes all his medical appointments in bright blue ink so he can see them. Despite being retired, he is busy, mostly with medical appointments. He hopes that soon he will become much less busy.

We do the work of healthcare. We also chat about life. That's my favorite part, the chatting.

We discuss my garden. It's a safe topic. Most people don't get too angry or offended about gardens. There are many unsafe topics these days. Gardening is safe.

I'm not a skilled gardener, but I am a passionate one. Healthcare and gardens are mixed together as we go about our visit.

Tomatoes, cucumbers, zucchini.
Blood pressure.
Marigolds, basil, snap peas.
Appetite.
Carrots, radishes, sunflowers.
Medications.

Blueberries, kale, collards.
Bowel habits.
Squirrels, rabbits, birds.
Activity.
Rabbits, racoons, rabbits.
Skin.
Moles, rabbits, rabbits, rabbits.
Curse you rabbits.

Today my patient is more excited than usual to discuss gardening. He wants to talk about gardening before we even start the business of healthcare. His seventy-year-old frame bounces on the exam table. Pale, bony feet kick back and forth.

What is he so excited about?

Not my calling.

Nursing was not my calling. Yet I chose it as my profession. Or perhaps it chose me. In my early twenties I stumbled into nursing. It was a regular paycheck. I didn't have to depend on anyone. I could work anywhere. It was a ticket to freedom. Continuously changing. I liked change. And it was challenging.

I liked helping people. Making a difference. Leaving my mark. Yet so many other ways exist to help. Ways that are cleaner and leave less scars on your soul. Jobs that don't require a shower at the end of the day. Placing your shoes in a bag to leave outside. Crying in the bathroom because someone you cared for died. Yet I stayed a nurse.

I liked the idea of healthcare yet I was naïve about what healthcare actually meant. I didn't understand healthcare and healthy care are often not the same thing.

Healthcare is doing. Healthcare is skills and tasks. It's checking things off a list. It's safety and protocols. It's billing and running a business. Care is provided but it's not always healthy care.

Healthy care is about being present. It's about helping people become healthier. It's joy and connection. It's caring for someone who can't care for themselves. Caring because you want to, because you can. It's taking the time to listen to a story or hold a hand. It's *soul care*. It's a state of human being, not human doing. It's learning by being silent. It's leading with your heart.

I discovered working in healthcare didn't always mean making people healthier. When I started out in nursing I couldn't imagine doing something that didn't make someone healthier, but it happens. Sometimes one system becomes healthier at the expense of another. People may die in spite of everything we do. People may also live in spite of everything they do. Yet I was interested in the idea of healthcare and soul care. Where do they intersect? Where might I help people to be healthy *and* practice healthcare at the same time?

I practiced healthcare (for years) before I began to see the outlines of what healthy care could be. How important it might be. How it might change my life. And the lives of my patients.

As a new nurse I quickly realized how much there was to learn. Many years were spent being aware of how much I didn't know. Striving to gain knowledge without making a critical mistake. Leaning on people around me who knew more. Asking questions. Listening to the answers. Observing. Learning and perfecting skills. Using every safety measure and double check, to make sure my learning did not get in the way of care. Learning to provide care and be caring at the same time. The learning never ends. I continued learning as a nurse.

I learned I needed a team. I was a nurse not a solitary island in the sea of medicine. I needed help. I believe nursing is a team sport. Without a team, without people who had my back, I was less effective. I was lonely. It took me time to realize the importance of a team for better patient care. And also the importance of being on a team for my own health, particularly my mental health.

Jobs that didn't promote teamwork did not suit me well. I didn't last long where the culture encouraged working on your own instead of collaboration. I didn't last long in the places where you could be shamed for making a mistake, left alone to figure it out. Instead of being left alone, I left. I sought out healthier teams. In those places I thrived.

Nursing was not my calling, but I stayed. I have stayed over two decades now. That fresh, new nurse from twenty years ago seems like a distant memory. I wonder if she would recognize the person I am today. I wonder if she may have benefitted from knowing some of what she would face, before she faced it. I wonder, if it has been worth it? If I could go back in time, would I do it all again?

I believe some of the answers are in the stories in this book.

For every story in this book there are hundreds more experiences I haven't written about. For every person in this book there are thousands more I met and cared for along the way. And with everything I've learned I believe there are still infinite new experiences to be had. Florence Nightingale had it right, we must always be learning. The day I stop wanting to learn is the day it is truly time to stop being a nurse.

Starting out

" The more I learn,
the more I realize
how much I don't know "

- Albert Einstein

4

Dentures.

When I was a student in nursing school I didn't know what dentures were. I didn't grow up around denture-wearing people. We saw my grandparents annually. If they had dentures I don't remember them. I missed any chapters on dentures or mention of them in the first two months of nursing school. Perhaps it was assumed, by the time you were in your early twenties, you'd been exposed to dentures. I was not.

My first practical rotation for nursing school was in a nursing home. We learned how to assist patients with what were called ADLs or Activities of Daily Living. Bathing. Walking. Dressing. Toileting. Brushing hair. Brushing teeth.

My very first patient was bed bound, meaning he could not get out of bed without significant (three people or a mechanical lift) assistance. His name was Maxmillian. He went by Max.

Max was covered in fragile, papery skin stretched across sharp bones and angles. His entire bath was performed with him in his bed. His gown and linens were changed for fresh ones. His hair, what remained, was washed. As I dried his hair it frizzed into a fluffy, white halo.

His teeth were brushed while he remained in bed as well. I had never brushed another person's teeth. In school we practiced on mannequins and plastic heads. Practice is helpful but it's not the same as a live, squishy, responsive person. Brushing your own teeth is not the same as brushing someone else's.

I started brushing Max's teeth. Hands shaking with nerves, my stomach clenched tight. *Do a good job. Do well. Do a good job.*

Moments into the tooth-brushing process something audibly pops. I feel and see Max's upper jaw shift in his mouth. Similar to a door sliding off the track, his upper jaw is no longer stable. Max sits in the bed, mouth open, calmly submitting to my fearful learning. My heart continues racing, hands trembling more, sweat now dripping down my back.

I attempt to "brush" his floating jaw back into place. It doesn't work.

Internal panic alarms start sounding.

I broke his jaw. On my first day, I broke someone. He's broken. I did that. Why is he not in pain? Why isn't he yelling? Mad at me? This makes no sense. Wouldn't I have pain if my jaw was broken? I should get help. Oh my God they're gonna kick me out of school. Two months in, I broke someone. I broke Max.

Shame. Guilt. Fear. They mix poorly with the acid in my already nervous stomach.

I push onward, continuing to work the toothbrush around Max's mouth. Determined to finish the job. To not break anything else. I hold back tears, but feel them threatening to spill. My eyelashes now damp at the edges.

I move to Max's lower teeth. Hoping his jaw will go back to where it belongs. He sits without moving. Mouth open. Eyes closed. Head back against a flat white pillow. Breathing. Grumbling. Breathing. Mumbling. The alarms cycle in my head over and over.

Don't break anything else. Get help. Don't break anything else. Get help. Don't break...

The cleaning of Max's lower teeth ends without significant events. His lower jaw appears intact. I put away my supplies. I am sweating, shaking, mortified. I broke my first patient.

Turning to face Max I tell him I will get the head nurse to assess his jaw. I'm sorry I broke him. The tears fall now and my voice breaks when I say the word "jaw." I look down, unable to hold eye contact with this man I broke.

Max blinks. Looks at me. Shakes his head. Mutters something. Harrumphs. Mutters again.

Max then reaches into his mouth and takes out a set of upper dentures. He pops out a lower set as well.

Holy crap he just took his jaw out. His whole upper jaw. And his lower jaw.... Waaaait.... Those are teeth. Teeth? That's not his jaw. What the hell? Portable teeth?

"Neth time," Max rasps at me, "tay thuu teeth ouu bufaw you bruth them."

He unceremoniously dumps the slick, gooey dentures in a small pink basin on his bedside table. Then closes his eyes and starts humming a song to himself, white hair flying all around.

Some days it's hard to remember being that young nursing student. She feels like a different person. Then other days, when I'm faced with learning something new, I feel like I'm right back in that nursing home room, brushing someone else's teeth. Talking to myself. Sweating and nervous. Trying not to cry. Praying it will get better.

Being a novice at anything is hard. Novice moments don't just arise when we're young. They happen all the time. This bears repeating - novice moments happen all the time. Even when you are a seasoned nurse.

The world is always changing. Sometimes the changes wear me down. Other times I love them. No matter what though, whether the change is welcome or fought against, it requires going through the first stage of not knowing what I don't know yet. Not knowing but being willing to learn. Not knowing and stepping into the not-knowing anyway. Knowing the only way to get to the-knowing side is to go through the awkward steps of not-knowing and learning.

5

Going home.

Years later I can still picture the thin skin hanging in folds off sharp, protruding bones. So pale I can see purple veins snaking along his arms and legs. Wrinkles on top of wrinkles. Hair floating in silvery wisps around his head. Round, brown age spots on his arms, face, and back. Both hands gripping his walker with hairy white knuckles, fingers taut on each rubber handle, not letting go. Knobby knees shaking but feet stable on the ground. Both feet in hospital-issue, gray slipper socks with white non-skid dots all over them. Wheezing as he stands there, like the lifelong smoker I know he is. Mint green hospital gown tied at the neck, but flapping open in the back. Wide open.

I approach Mr. Jackson cautiously. It's my second day on the unit as a nursing assistant. I am green with a capital G. And young, so very young and inexperienced. Now, on my second day, here is this man dressed in an open gown and slipper socks, nothing else. He is seven decades older than me. He stands in the middle of the busy hallway. His gown wide open in the back, like a cape being worn in reverse.

"Are you alright sir? Do you need to sit down? Let's get you a chair." I rush in eager to help.

I am here to help! Oh boy, someone to help!

Hack. Cough. Wheeze. Wheeze. Sharp, dark eyes under hairy caterpillar eyebrows whip around to look at me. To assess. The caterpillars draw together. He takes my measure.

"Are you a nurse?" Wheeeeze. Cough. The caterpillars wiggle. The knees shake. The feet stay planted.

"Uh... no sir. A nursing assistant. Sir, I'm going to tie your gown in the back. It's ummmm, open..." Cautiously I walk around to the bare backside. Let's take care of the business of modesty. *Modesty first, then a chair*, I think. *I can do this.*

"No!" Mr. Jackson barks sharply, then wheezes again. "Untied it for a reason. Don't meddle, girl." The caterpillars come together. He glares at me from beneath them.

Oh goodness. Why? Why would he do that? Does he need a new gown? A different gown? Maybe a second gown, to use like a robe? I look around for help, anyone. Anyone besides me. But there is no one, just me and Mr. Mostly-exposed-Jackson.

"Errrrm sir, why... why did you untie your gown? What... why are you standing in the middle of the hallway? Let's take you back to your room now..." *Regroup. If we can't tackle modesty we'll work on safety! I can help!*

"No." He barks and wheezes at me again. The hairy caterpillars rest together, then separate. He pauses. Appraises. "Perhaps... you can get me a nurse..." The eyes under the caterpillars look hopeful. Cough. Wheeze. Wobble. Gray slipper socks shuffle.

"Sure sir, I can do that... Are you having pain? Are you tired? Let's get you back to bed first, then I'll get a nurse..." *I can help. I can help. I can help.*

Again, he barks at me, "No. I need a nurse, here in the hall-way." He looks around, everyone rushing this way and that. No one pausing. The caterpillars look at me again. "They're all too fast though."

He whispers the last part on a wheeze.

"Too fast," he echoes. The words so quiet, so small. The second time I barely hear them. I step closer.

He sounds defeated. Sad. The caterpillars droop at the edges. *Do eyebrows get sad?*

Again I try, still not understanding, not grasping what he needs. Only grasping that I need to help him. Me so young and blind, him so determined.

"Sir, let's get back to your room and I'll find your nurse. We can do this..."

"No. You are *not* listening girl. You are not a nurse. I need a nurse. I can't go home until I get a nurse." Cough. Wheeze. Wobble. Glare.

I'm confused and it must clearly show on my face. He sighs. The caterpillars rise up and his eyes sparkle for a moment, then dim. He suddenly seems every one of his ninety-plus years as he stands here in the hallway.

"I can't go home until I catch a nurse. An' I can't catch one 'cause they never stop moving. Nurse Ratchet over there..." He nods the caterpillars towards the charge nurse who is now leaning against the counter, watching us. Cough. Wheeze. Wobble. Shuffle.

"Nurse IronBalls says I can't go home 'til I get outta bed and catch a nurse." Wheeze. Wobble. "You are not a nurse. So...." Wobble. Cough.

"No... you cannot take me back to bed. I have to catch a nurse. I want to go home." Cough. Wheeze. Wobble. Wheeze. Glare.

Then the curtain lifts. I see him. Finally. Behind the caterpil-lars, the open gown, the wheezing, wobbling, coughing, shaky legs, papery white skin, wispy silvery hair. There he is. His pride. His strength. His resolve.

This man untied his gown on purpose, like bait. He stands in the middle of one of the busiest hallways in the hospital. He is going to catch a nurse. He is going home.

Oooh. I want to help. I so badly want to help. But I cannot. This man wants to go home. Oh boy.

Decades into a career in nursing I remember Mr. Jackson and this hallway. In fact I carry him with me everyday. It was one of the busiest units in the hospital where I worked as a nursing assistant. I was so painfully new to this business of providing care for people. Mr. Jackson taught me an invaluable lesson on my second day of work. Do not assume anything. Ever. Do not assume I know what people want.

People have their own motivations and their own agendas. They have wants and needs. They have dreams and goals. The hospital staff may *need* them to do something, like tie their gown or sit down, but that does not mean they will do it.

If I really want to provide care for someone I have to know what *they* want. What are *their goals? Their dreams.* Not mine. Otherwise I am just as inept as a two-day old nursing assistant trying to get a ninety-plus- year-old man to tie his gown and go back to bed.

Start where your patient is. Not where you want to be. Not where you're trying to get to.

Start where your patient is, even if he's half-naked in the hospital hallway.

6

Cheese crackers.

I was a few months into my career as a nursing assistant when I spent the evening with a seventy-five-year-old man. He'd undergone emergency surgery earlier that day. We ate cheese crackers and drank beer for most of the night. Except, I did not actually eat or drink anything. Neither did he.

I worked swing and night shifts on a busy post-surgical floor while going to nursing school during the day. I was still young enough, the odd hours and lack of sleep didn't affect me much. Most nights I attended to patient's basic needs. I was assigned to a group of nurses to help with patient transfers, toileting needs, baths, walks and so on.

Some nights I was assigned to sit with patients. "Sitting" literally meant sitting in a room with a patient. These patients were usually confused due to dementia, delirium, or drugs. The concern was the patient would get out of bed. They might fall or be injured before someone could help. So a nursing assistant (like me) was assigned to sit with the patient. Sit. Sit. Sit.

Sit and watch. Sit. And watch. And sit.

On this particular night, I received a quick verbal report from the previous sitter.

"He's really confused but funny. You're gonna have a long but good night. Don't let him get outta bed." That was it.

I enter the dimly lit hospital room. Pierce, the patient, lays in bed attached to multiple cords and wires. He smiles when I come in, a reassuring greeting from a confused patient. Sometimes they yell, scream, spit, attack, grunt. A smile is great.

Pierce points to the chair next to his bed and hoarsely says "have a seat have a seat have a seat havaseaaa....," eventually trailing off. His eyes, a little bit glassy, follow me, then close. He snores. A low, deep, throaty rumble fills the room each time he exhales.

Alright, I can sit. It's why I'm here anyway. To sit with you.

I sit. I watch. I sit.

When Pierce reawakens I introduce myself and explain why I'm in his room. Where he is. Why he's in the hospital. The plan for the evening. I will be with him for the night...

I trail off mid-explanation as his glassy eyes focus in front of him (not on me). He reaches into the space that hovers over his legs.

Pierce nods and smiles at me while stretching his right arm further forward. Reaching to his right, fingers rolling, as if playing notes on a piano. He grasps what he wants in the air. Pulling this particular piece of air back to himself. Right hand now firmly holding some unseen object about three inches wide. He places the object on a flat (and equally invisible) surface in front of him. Using both hands he reaches into the air above his invisible object. Pierce places his hands together as if clasping something. He then spreads his hands apart about six inches. (Imagine someone opening a cereal box.)

Glassy eyes semi-focused on the prized object, concentrating. With his left hand he now holds the unseen object. With his right hand he reaches up over an invisible threshold. Down into the depths of the object goes his hand. Rummaging around while grunting, his fingers move and dig in the thin air above his lap.

He smiles at me. Then he says, "Hang on, I'll getchya summa good uns."

I'm riveted. Never having seen anything like this before. I have not figured out what he is doing. Thoughts float around in my head. *Ummmm what are you doing sir? Do I need to call the nurse? Please stay in bed. What. Are. You. Doing?*

He pulls his right hand out from the top of the invisible object. The right hand extends towards me as if cupping an object. He glares at the ECG cord that impedes his progress until it snaps off.

Pierce smiles, "cheese crackers. Yum!" He is delighted. *Yum! Ah. He thinks he has a box of crackers. Cheese ones.*

I get up to reattach the ECG cord he popped off, tucking it under his gown. "Uh, no sir," I say, "those are not cheese crackers. I think you may be seeing things."

The smile fades. His heart rate goes up on the monitor. His right hand shakes as it continues to offer the crackers.

"I gotcha the good uns," he says. "Ya have to try 'em. Yummmm."

"Er, no thank you sir. It's time to sleep now. Recover from surgery... It's late. How 'bout you close your eyes and rest..." I trail off looking at the man in the bed who is getting more agitated. Shaking his cracker-laden right hand at me. He tries to push himself to a more upright position in the bed.

Nononono. No. You are supposed to be resting sir. Rest!

"Take 'em," he says. "They're good." Glassy eyes glare at me. The smile is gone. Right hand wobbles. I hear his heart rate rising on the monitor in the corner. He strains to move, to get out of bed. *No. no. no. no. Oh no...*

"Stay calm," I say to him. To myself. "Just breathe. It's okay."

It's not okay, it's not okay, it's not okay. No no no no…. You are not supposed to get up. It's not okay….

"Sir, um, Pierce… there are no cheese crackers…" Another attempt to maintain reality.

Reorient. Keep calm. Stay in bed. Don't let him get up.

Pierce's eyes flash with increased agitation. He pushes more, trying to get his legs over the edge of the bed. This is the one thing he is not supposed to do. The one thing I am here to prevent him from doing.

Oh no oh no oh no oh no. Stay calm. Breathe. Arrrrrggggh. Why won't this guy just sleep? I don't know what to do. I. Don't. Know. What. To. Do.

"You have to stay in bed sir. You had surgery today. Please don't get up."

Where is the nurse? Am I going to get in trouble for this? What if he actually gets up? Argh. Crappity crap.

"Please, Pierce, please…" My hands tremble as much as his while I gently try to keep him in his bed.

"Eat the cheese crackers!" he yells.

I stop. Look at him. Right hand outstretched, holding air. Sitting in a hospital bed. Hair matted flat on one side, sticking up on the other. Yoked to the bed with wires and cords. I think about what I have been taught.

Do not agree with the hallucinations. Help people by giving them reality. Reorient them. Gently remind them where they are. Why they are there. Remind them what is real. The cheese crackers are not real.

You are in a hospital. You had surgery. You may not be fully awake yet after anesthesia. I am here to help you stay safe. Basically, do not eat the cheese crackers.

"Eat. The. Cheese. Crackers!" Pierce roars, startling me from my thoughts. I expect someone to come in. Rescue me.

Someone out in the hallway must be hearing this...Please help me.

Pierce's legs inch closer to the edge of the bed. Both our heart rates rise. Both our hands tremble, his from exertion, mine from anxiety.

His face is blotchy with effort. Mine is frozen.

I make a decision... I eat the cheese crackers.

He calms down. He stays in bed.

The change is almost immediate.

He does not fall or injure himself.

I eat the salami he slices. I drink the can of light beer.

At this point I'm all in.

He drifts off to sleep around 3 am.

The nurse comes in to assess Pierce a couple times during the shift. I try to explain what happened. I ate the crackers-that-were-not-really-crackers. Then he calmed down.

Guilt. Did I do the right thing? What is the right thing? I don't know. This is not what I was taught.

The nurse seems unconcerned by it all. "As long as he doesn't hurt himself," she says. "He needs to stay in bed for now." She didn't seem to know about what I had been taught in school. Don't eat the crackers. *But I ate the crackers. And it helped...*

Pierce wakes up around 7 am, just before I'm leaving for class. He looks at me. Despite being groggy he is much more alert. It's the eyes; they're clear now. He knows his name. Knows he had surgery. Knows he is in the hospital.

He tells me he is hungry. Had the best dream about crackers, salami, and beer. I smile and ask if he was dreaming about cheese crackers in particular.

This is the first time I remember being confronted by the difference between what I am *taught* to do and what I *actually* do. The nursing student I was twenty years ago still believed the textbook was always the way to do it. Follow the rules. Do what you're taught. The book has all the answers.

Except sometimes real life hasn't read the book. Sometimes real life doesn't know there's a book. However when I was just starting out, a brand new nurse with so much to learn, the book was a good place to start. I figured out quickly though, the book is only a starting point.

Sometimes to care for someone, meet them where they are, with their cheese crackers and beer, I have to make it up as I go along. I improvise, striving to do the best I can in that moment. I use the textbook, the evidence, the plan. But I also use everything else I've learned or seen or experienced along the way.

Sometimes, I eat the cheese crackers, and definitely drink the beer.

7

Howl.

Labor and Delivery (L&D) was a required rotation when I was in nursing school. Before being allowed on the unit with a nurse preceptor and actual patients, learning must be done. I recall reading a few chapters. Listening to a couple lectures. Watching a video of a live, vaginal birth.

L&D is mildly horrifying and extremely fascinating to me. I desperately want to see a live birth.

In my first week on the L&D unit I am paired with a nurse preceptor who is mostly "hands-off" when it comes to my education. Somehow, I know immediately I am not a welcome visitor in her world. Her method of teaching is to toss me into the deep end and see if I sink or swim.

I never cried during this rotation, but I also wouldn't say I swam either. More of a sloppy dog paddle.

On my third shift of the week, my preceptor and I receive report from the night nurse. After report the two nurses start chatting about lunch, weekend plans, someone they don't like who's working that day... I awkwardly stand behind my preceptor's chair and wonder about the patient in the room. I shuffle my feet which makes a bit of noise. *Oops.*

The night nurse glances up. My preceptor turns around.

"Go in and check things out. Report back to me. I have coffee to drink," my preceptor tells me. Then she turns back to the night nurse. Her back, covered in pink scrubs with smiley faces and hearts, seems incongruous to me.

This is my third practical rotation in nursing school. The first was at a nursing home, the second was an outpatient clinic, and now L&D, in a hospital. I know how to check a blood pressure. I can listen to a heart beat and lung sounds. I am good with dentures. But a woman in labor... I'm not sure what I'm supposed to be doing. But I don't ask. I'm too scared. Too uncertain of what I am supposed to know and what I don't know.

Okay, I can check out a room. Maybe the patient. Well, if she has dentures, at least I know what to do with those...

I enter a dark hospital room. Shades down. Curtains drawn. A bedside lamp glows. It's quiet in the room. My eyes adjust. I spot Felicia doubled over the backside of a hospital room chair, hips rocking side to side, humming quietly. Her head drapes down towards the chair seat. She rocks back and forth to a rhythm she hums.

Felicia glances up briefly, her eyes lock on mine. Then she drops her head and resumes swaying and humming. As she sways the humming turns into a howl that is long and sustained. Building to a crescendo then dying off slowly. The howl fills the dark room with noise, color, substance. I slowly back out of the room.

"Um, the room is fine. It's dark with one light on. Um, Felicia is swaying and humming, by a chair. Then she howled. So, yeah. That's it." I report to my preceptor who is just finishing her first coffee.

My preceptor looks at me like I might be the worst nursing student ever. At least it feels that way. She shakes her head and I follow her back into the hospital room (despite no invitation to do so).

Felicia is alone. No friends, no family, no partner. Admitted to the L&D unit about four hours before we arrived this morning. Felicia does not have an epidural and is free to move around the room. My preceptor helps her into the bed then starts her work.

After assessing her, my preceptor tells me Felicia is dilated to eight centimeters. The goal is ten centimeters. She's close.

Once Felicia dilates to ten centimeters, she can push (if things look good). I nod eagerly, as if I know what this all means. Felicia is not interested in drugs, interventions, birthing balls, warm baths, or much of anything other than get-this-thing-out-of-me....

Then she, "howls."

A howl accompanies each contraction. It's shocking, amazing, terrifying. Primal. I could hear the howl throughout the whole L&D unit when I walked in that morning. I had no idea it would be my patient who was howling.

Felicia dilates the remaining two centimeters in less than two hours. After a quick check from the doctor, it is time to push. My books, lectures, the video we watched, they all prepared me for stirrups, lying on your back, breathing exercises. Pushing in coordination with cues from the nurse or doctor. I stand in a corner, nervous and excited, observing and trying to learn as much as possible.

My preceptor tells me I can be Felicia's breathing coach since there isn't anyone with her.

"You do know how to breathe, right?" asks my preceptor.

I do! I think in my head. I do know how to breathe! I am ready. Sort of. Nervous. Wanting to help, like any overeager student nurse. *I can breathe. I can help. Let's do this.*

I step out of my corner, ready to help with breathing. My preceptor stands across the room from me. During a pause between contractions Felicia clambers up onto the hospital bed squatting at the head of it. Her feet are spread just wider than hip distance apart on the pillow. Her bare bottom facing the rest of the room. She grasps the headboard while in full squat position, head bent down as if in prayer, loose hospital gown around her shoulders.

What about breathing? Who taught her this? To climb up? To squat? Why? What? How does she know? This was not in my book. Or the video. Hey, what about breathing exercises? What am I supposed to do now?

I look across the room at my nurse preceptor. This person who's supposed to be taking the lead, teaching me what to do. She stands there, mouth agape. Pink scrubs with smiley faces smiling back at me. No words come out. Eyes wide and unblinking. Apparently this was not in her books either.

Please do something. Teach me something. Do something, other than drink coffee and occasionally glare at me. This woman is now squatting on a bed. Can she do this? Climb onto a bed and squat on it? This was not in my book...

Then, "HOWL" escapes from Felicia's mouth. My internal monologue is interrupted. A groan comes from somewhere deep. Felicia's head remains bowed forward. Both her hands grasp the headboard. Her feet firmly rooted on the head of the mattress as she squats, groans, sways, hums. Howls again.

"HOWL," bounces around the room and off the walls, reverberating in the corners. Followed by another deeper groan. Then a pause. Then silence.

Time stands still. I hold my breath. Nothing moves. Then Felicia's head rises. I follow her gaze as she looks up at the drab, white ceiling panels. Blinks. Her eyes close. Her mouth opens. One final

"HOWL" echoes off the walls of the small hospital room. I watch her, then I blink and in that moment it happens. Onto the bed slides a brand new little life.

Gooey. Slippery. Pink. Deep charcoal black hair matted to its head.

Oh, do not slip off the bed little life. Welcome to the world little human...little miracle.

No doctor is in the room because of unblinking eyes and mouth gaping. Shock, I think, perhaps she is shocked? Then everything is a blur of motion, sound, color, fluids. So many fluids. More people appear as if by magic. A doctor, more nurses. It gets busy. I stay by the head of the bed. Observing to learn. Unable to participate beyond that.

Felicia lets out a few more whimpers but her howling is done. The cord is clamped. The new little life is wrapped and swaddled by an able nurse. Nurses change the linens on the bed. Felicia is repositioned. Bed rails are put up. Felicia meets her baby.

In the midst of all this efficient nursing care, while squatting, howling, then being turned around, Felicia managed to pull the headboard out from the bed frame. I take it. This is my only memorable contribution to the whole affair. I slide it back into place. I am grateful for the time I spent working as a nursing assistant already. I know how to put a headboard back onto a hospital bed. Nothing else about this room or this experience is familiar. But a headboard, I can handle.

When I reflect back on this day, I *remember* a few things.

I *remember* how it feels to be unwelcomed. That deep, uncomfortable ache in my gut. The itchy-twitchy sense in my hands. I want to shrink and take up less space. I assumed nurses would be happy to train new nurses. This is not always the truth.

Some nurses are wonderful preceptors. And some have other talents. And some wonderful preceptors have bad days or weeks. When you're a nursing student you have to be prepared to roll with it, whatever "it" may be. I'm not saying, to allow yourself to be abused, put down or bullied, but I am saying sometimes your learning is comes by doing, and other times it's by observing. Be ready to take what you can get.

I *remember* knowing so little about birth. I assumed births took place lying down, in beds, with breathing exercises. That's what my book, lectures, and video prepared me for. That's what movies and TV show you. I learned reality doesn't always follow the book. Just as there are a million different women giving birth, there are a million different ways to do it.

I *remember* thinking the birth of a baby would be attended by the mom (obviously) and a whole crowd of people. Everyone excited to welcome a new life into the world. That is not always the case. In the same way there are a million different women birthing a million different ways, there are also a million different types of families. The small glimpse you get in the hospital does not always reflect what home looks like. Don't make assumptions about support or the lack thereof based on what you see in the hospital, in a snapshot of time.

And finally, I remember that when I'm the one doing the training, I can be kind and welcoming. There are not perfect learning experiences every day, like seeing a live birth in L&D. And as it turns out, that was not an ideal learning experience, even though it's the one thing I wanted to see. I can help those who come behind me learn as they enter their new profession. I can hopefully leave a kinder, gentler trail, than what was often left for me. And if a headboard gets pulled out, well, I can fix that too.

8

Cycles.

It is my first day as a real nurse in the Intensive Care Unit (ICU). It is my first patient as a real nurse. Not a student nurse. Not a being-trained nurse. As a fully-made-it, passed-my-boards, here-is-your-assignment, go-get-the-job-done nurse. No preceptor. No training wheels.

Just me and my patient.

I think I'm ready. I think I know so much. I want so badly to prove all the time and energy people have put into training me has paid off. I can do this. I *will* do this. Pride. Butterflies. Excitement. Nerves. All blended with a deep desire to do well.

Do right. Save lives. Help others.

It is also my first time seeing someone die.

I am on the job for three hours.

John has no family or friends. None that anyone knows about. He has previously been admitted to this same hospital for various ailments and issues. A "frequent flier." He signed papers declaring his wishes to not be resuscitated. John re-signed those papers each time he was admitted. (Except last night, because he never woke up.) No CPR. No rescue breathing. No interventions. No thank you.

When it's time, it's time. Simply put, peace out world.

Signed, John.

John was picked up off the street from the midst of a cavern of boxes, a shopping cart, and a broken park bench. Brought in by medics.

Who called the medics? How did the medics find him? Was he awake then? I wonder these things as I listen to report from the night nurse.

John is in bad shape. Heart beating, lungs breathing, but unresponsive. His entire body cold. Hands and feet purple. When I assess him I can't feel a pulse anywhere except in his neck. I start my day believing John will live. I believe I will save him.

John does not recover this time.

I'm the only other person in the room when he dies. I hold his hand and stand there. Being. Just being. *It hurts to be this still. This non-moving. What can I do???*

Three hours into my first shift. Already I do not know what to do. I am ready to save lives. I know how to do CPR, give medications, defibrillate irregular heart rhythms. I know how to pump life into those who are temporarily lifeless. I know how to start IV lines, call codes, fill rooms to capacity with people whose entire purpose is to save a life.

I do not know what to do when there is nothing to be done. I did not know there was a time when nothing *could* be done.

I stand there. In a room filled with machines and equipment dedicated to saving lives. A cart in the corner is filled with nothing but medications, fluids, bits and bobbles for life saving. I use none of it. I push down the urge to press the blue button over the bed. *Call a code. Flood the room with people. Do something.*

I hold John's cool, purple hand. I honor his wishes to not be resuscitated. His breathing shudders, gasps, gurgles, rasps. My breathing is shallow, nervous, quick.

His heart slows. Beats. Slows more. Beats again.

My heart pounds, races, strains. *There must be something I can do. Anything.*

Then, suddenly, he's gone. I feel the room change. Without looking at the monitors, I know he is gone. I feel for a presence that was there a moment ago. It's not there now. I continue to hold his hand.

I didn't know the room would feel different. I didn't know it would change so quickly, or at all. A last breath, then nothing. Stillness. There is nothing I can do. No doing. Just being.

I'm alone in the sterile, white room with flashing lights and beeps for company. It's the first time I consider the difference between a body and a soul.

Then the charge nurse rushes in and asks why I am holding John's hand. I didn't realize I still was. I let go, hesitantly.

The nurse in the pod next to me turns off the monitors and beeps. She says she'll grab the body bag. She's calm, cool efficiency.

The cleaning crew arrives thirty minutes later. The paperwork is completed, signed, filed. Just over one hour later there is another patient in the room. Another life fighting to live. My second patient. My second patient as a real nurse.

Life. Death. Beginnings. Endings. Sometimes there is nothing to be done. No doing. Just being. *But how can there be no doing when all I have learned, all I have been taught, is doing? I only know how to do.*

Just being. Be present. Bear witness.

To life. To death. As it cycles.

In school I learned so much of the doing. There are so many tasks and the learning curve is quite steep. As a new nurse I want to learn all the things I need to know to be safe and do the job well.

Yet somewhere in between all of that doing is something intangible and beautiful that makes nursing unlike any other profession. It's the opportunity to connect and I think it's one of the most powerful things nurses are able to do. For me it's most evident in those moments when life is arriving or when life is ending, but it can show up anywhere or anytime. It's those moments when you can feel the energy in the room shift, the air change, and you know there is something more than what we can see. The world keeps turning but your life and that of your patient are forever changed, because you found a way to connect.

9

Dirt.

Hunt is a rancher from a small town in the middle of nowhere. A town surrounded by fields and farms, populated by hard working folk and cows. Lots of cows. He has really unfortunate genetics, resulting in a massive heart attack in his mid-forties. Despite his regrettable genetics, he's fortunate he has people around him who know CPR and call 911. He's airlifted from his small town to a hospital in a big town. He has heart surgery, recovers well for about 12 hours, then has complications. He has another heart surgery, recovers again, then has more complications. He has a third heart surgery. He's still alive in spite of everything. Recovery though, is a bit slower after the third surgery.

Hunt wakes up in the ICU thirteen days after the third surgery. When I meet him I am a fairly new ICU nurse. I am in that phase of learning that feels like drinking from a fire hose. All that knowledge flowing in fast and furious. *Can I hold it all? Can I learn it all fast enough?* I am in that phase of learning where I am focused on all the tasks, all the things I need to do to be proficient.

One morning, a few days after he wakes up following his third surgery, I help Hunt sit up at the edge of the bed. He tells me it hurts but not in those words. I learn new words the day Hunt sits up on the edge of the bed. New ways of describing something unpleasant.

A few days later I help Hunt move from his bed to a chair. He has a lot of fancy words to say about that process as well. Phrases and words to describe something he doesn't want to do.

The day after that, two other nurses, two physical therapists, and I help him start walking with a walker. There are more choice words and colorful descriptions for the walker, the hospital, and walking in general. Enough colorful descriptions for each of us to hear something new. Even the long-time, craggy veterans of the unit discover there are new ways to express displeasure about walking.

Hunt hates the ICU. He hates the wires and cords, the IV lines tethering him to everything. He hates the electronics, the beeps, and the harsh white lights. He hates the shiny metal, sterile all-of-it. He hates the window that looks outside. Yet he likes being alive. This is the only thing he is agreeable about. He likes life. But recovering and returning to his old life is very slow.

As the days progress it becomes less clear if recovery will happen at all.

Then on his twenty-eighth day in the ICU something unexpected happens. Hunt cries.

To say it is surprising would be a gross understatement. It is a big, sobbing, ugly cry that starts when I walk into his room for my shift. I freeze.

"Close the curtains," he grumps at me.

I do, feeling largely unprepared for this, whatever it is. Wishing I could turn around and sneak back out the door. Wishing I am carrying the code pager and it might beep. I would rather be doing CPR and running a code, then watching my patient cry.

Despite my internal monologue, I sit with him. *What else can I do?*

Hunt cries. I stay frozen.

I wonder... Is this pain? Anger? Depression? Why now? Why my shift? Doesn't anyone need me anywhere else? Did he do this with Diane? She has twenty plus years experience for goodness sake. She's great. She didn't mention this in report. Anyone else besides me... Anyone...

I sit frozen, hand him tissues, one after another. Not knowing what to say to this rancher who survived a heart attack and three heart surgeries. This rancher, who is now slowly decaying in the ICU day-by-day. Sometimes having no idea what to say serves me well. Silence creates space.

Hunt pauses. Blows his nose. Hiccups. Wipes his eyes and starts talking in his gravelly drawl. It's dirt. He misses dirt.

He misses the smell of dirt. He misses being outside. Fresh air. Raw earth. This ICU does not have dirt. This ICU does not allow flowers. Nothing lives here except people. No dirt. He yearns for dirt. And his old life. But mostly for being outside and for dirt.

So I find a wheelchair, blankets, portable monitors, a rescue pack, oxygen, and a whole bunch of other equipment. I find my charge nurse because I need help. Lots of help. I have a vague idea, if we can get Hunt to dirt he will get better. He might even get better enough to transfer out of the ICU. He might eventually go home, to his dirt. But I have no idea how to actually make it all happen. My charge nurse that day is one of those ass-kicking, knows-what-to-do in any situation kind of people. He is on it.

"He needs dirt? The grumpy old bastard wants dirt? That will get him out of my ICU? Well, sheee-it. Let's make that happen."

All of us have been watching Hunt slowly waste away for weeks following his third surgery. "Done," says my charge nurse. Now I *know* it will happen.

On his twenty-eighth day in the ICU, Hunt goes outside. Accompanied by an armada of ICU staff. To a small patio with a few spindly, sad, droopy plants. The plants, despite being sad, are growing in dirt. Hunt sits. Smells. Smiles. I never knew he could smile. From the way his face stretches, then doesn't quite relax, it looks like it has been a while. But, it also looks like he used to smile. We wheel him back inside ten minutes later. That's all it takes.

Hunt walks out of the hospital seven days later. After a month in the ICU, he walks. Not in a wheelchair. Not on a stretcher. He walks, with a smile. He goes back to his ranch and his dirt.

Every nurse on that unit worked with Hunt for at least one shift and watched him slowly fail and fade. I suspect any nurse on that unit would have been thrilled to see a little fight in him. Any nurse would have found a way to get him dirt.

I don't know why he finally let it all go when I came on shift that day, but I'm grateful he did. My discomfort with the situation, my frozen fear, created silence and space for Hunt to cry. My desire to have a concrete, solvable problem or task led to a field trip outside of the ICU. My team made it happen. Thank goodness he gave me something concrete to do, "get me dirt," or this story could have a very different ending.

Taking Hunt outside for a "field trip" remains one of my favorite examples of what a group of scrappy, innovative nurses can do when motivated. Everyone on the unit had connected with Hunt on some level and wanted to see him be able to go back home. Everyone was willing to think a bit outside the box and help him get there. The end result was a quick trip to dirt. The turn around was almost immediate. Sometimes you just have to figure out what motivates your patient and the results can be amazing.

I can still see Hunt, in my mind, when he sat outside and smiled on the patio. He was surrounded by an armada of ICU staff, equipment and dirt. Yet it was like watching a feeble flame come roaring to life. His fight returned. I hope if I'm ever in the hospital I have a little bit of the fight Hunt had in him to get me back home to what matters most. I hope today, nearly twenty years later, he's still alive. Living well on his ranch with his cows. And his dirt.

10

The count.

At the end of every shift two nurses do "the count." The two nurses are generally the charge nurse and a randomly selected nurse from the unit. The nurses who do "the count" rotate. It's not always the same people. "The count" is literally counting all the narcotics and controlled substances in the Pyxis (locked medication dispenser). It's done to ensure the number of vials or ampules actually in there matches what the computer "thinks" should be in the machine. Our unit works twelve-hour shifts so "the count" happens twice a day. It is almost always correct. Except for the odd times it is not.

I worked on the night shift. The night shift crew was an eclectic group. Some nurses are young, some old. Some have families or small kids. Most have worked nights for a long time. Many like it for the schedule or the extra differential pay. Either way, unusual personalities seem to be more abundant on night shift compared to the day shift.

Tammi was a night-shift ICU nurse for over forty years. She was probably the most unusual of the bunch.

Tammi lived just outside the city in a yurt. She lived in a yurt long before glamping and yurts were "in." She did not have running water or electricity. She lived "off the grid," in her words. She bathed occasionally often smelling of some mixture of smoke, fresh dirt, musk, and body odor. Her graying hair was something between uncombed and dreadlocks but didn't really fit either category. She wore it pulled back in some semblance of a bun. Her scrubs were always clean. Her shoes were cleaner than mine. She got her work done. She was part of the team.

Tammi, when asked, described herself as eccentric. She had peculiar habits and routines she followed. Tammi read most nights, large, dogeared, paperback novels. Sometimes a nurse would find her sleeping at her work pod, head on her book, loud snoring. The nurse who found her would wake her up. Everyone would go on about their night.

Sometimes when Tammi woke up her words were a little slurred. She didn't quite make sense. She might start reciting random poetry. Her eyes might be a little glassy or unfocused. But then she would drink from her coffee mug. Do a few jumping jacks and push ups in the hallway. All would be right again. Someone wakes her up. She gets back to work. Tammi is part of the team.

Looking back, there were signs. But when you're part of a team you don't always see the signs clearly. I was a new ICU nurse. I was young, innocent. I did not see the signs. I would not have known what to look for.

The night it all changed is similar to any other night. Until no one can find Tammi. She isn't asleep at her work pod. She isn't asleep in the break room. No one talked with her in the past hour. No one can find her, anywhere. My patient assignment is geographically next to hers that night. I agree to cover one of her patients until she is found. The nurse who has patients on the other side of Tammi's assignment agrees to do the same. Healthcare continues without interruption. Nurses continue to search for Tammi.

Eventually it's determined the staff bathroom is locked. Despite repeated knocking there is no answer. Everyone but Tammi is accounted for. *Is someone in there? Is Tammi?*

No one knows. Worry starts to spread. *Has Tammi suffered a heart attack or stroke? She is older... Is she lying on the floor unable to respond?*

We work in an ICU. Worst-case-scenario thinking is our bread and butter. I continue to take care of my patients and Tammi's. I keep my head down, doing my job. But I worry and wonder along with my team.

Eventually, the locked bathroom door is opened by force. Tammi is found down. On the floor. Barely breathing. Palest white gray skin. Very still. Her head rests in a puddle of her own drool. There is a single syringe attached to a needle, still in her arm. Blood coagulates on her arm around it. Vials for fentanyl, morphine, and midazolam are on the floor. Some are used.

A code is called for one of our own, one of our nurses, one of our team. There's a transfer to the ER. The bathroom is cleaned. It all happens quickly. A blur of motion and noise. I stick to my patients and patient of Tammi's I am covering for. I do my job. I do not want to see what I am seeing. I do not want to feel what I am feeling.

Why is this happening? What was she doing? Why? What? Why? I don't understand. This is not what I signed up for. This is not nursing. This is not what nurses do. This is not nursing... is it? Fear, I feel fear and uncertainty in my stomach. My legs are jittery and weak.

None of this makes sense to me. It doesn't fit what I *think* I *know* about nursing. Nurses take care of people. Nurses give people medications when they need them. Nurses don't take those medications, those drugs. But nurses are people too... I realize there is so much I do not know. My orderly picture of what is and is not a nurse starts to fray at the edges, maybe even tear a little. *Do right. Save lives. Help others. Provide care. But what if you need care? What if you need help?*

Decades later I still don't really want to see, hear, or feel when I think of this night. It's traumatic, still. Looking back, I wonder how long it was going on? Were the nights "the count" was off the same nights Tammi worked? Was "the count" off on other nights? Was anyone else on my team using? Was anyone else on my team suffering? Will this happen to me someday if I do this work long enough? Nurses are people. *Normal, flawed, people...*

A lot of my innocence and naivete as a new nurse was destroyed that night. My picture of a nurse was never quite the same. The world never looked quite the same. For me, Tammi became a painful, cautionary tale.

As a nurse I've learned over the past twenty years that everyone, every single person I have met (nurse or otherwise), has challenges and demons. We're all fighting with or against something. Addiction, anxiety, depression, deceit, hubris, the list goes on and on. Despite our shortcomings though, we are all worthy of love and human connection. Despite our flaws we all count.

Get help. It sounds simple (just those two words) but I recognize it's truly not. Ask for help. Reach out. Be brave. Get help. If you're struggling, using, addicted, thinking about using - get help. If you see someone you think might be struggling, don't turn a blind eye - ask them if they need help (they'll probably say no). But at least ask - maybe you catch them at the right time, the right moment, when they're ready to get help. You don't have to know what to do next. There are resources, support groups, 12-step programs, sponsors, second chances (and third chances). Remember, we all count.

11

Belonging.

The first years of nursing are spent learning the skills. The doing. The nuts and bolts. How to organize the day. How to take report and give report. How to call a physician. How to ask for an order. How to decipher an order. Orders were hand-written on paper charts when I started. Now it's all digital.

How to get patients safely and cleanly into bed. Out of a chair. Off a commode. Into the bathroom. Down a hall. Back home. How to pass medications, inject medications, flush medications, hang medications. So. Many. Medications. And so many safety protocols. Doing CPR. Changing dressings. Returning from surgery. Going to surgery. Doing. Doing. Doing.

The first months, while full of painful learning, are somewhat blissful. I don't know how much I don't know. Until suddenly I do. From that moment on, when I realize the mole hill is actually a mountain, it is sheer terror. I down Tums every night for the heartburn, then Zantac, then Pepcid. My stomach churns constantly with acid, bile, and nerves. I am on high alert all the time. Aware of how much I have to learn and desperate to learn it quickly without making a fatal mistake. My sleep suffers, my temper flares often. I become unbearable everywhere except work. But I am saved.

As a brand new nurse I work the night shift on an ICU. Most of the nurses on the unit have worked there for years. It seems to me they have seen and experienced just about everything to be experienced in an ICU. They teach me so much of what they know and I frantically take in as much as I can. Despite my shortening temper, nightly Tums, and constant stress I love what I am doing.

After about six months on the unit I am assigned to carry the code pager. The code pager goes off (or beeps) if someone, anywhere in the hospital, calls a code (meaning someone is not breathing or their heart has stopped). The act of carrying the code pager increases my "stomach distress." I find myself running to the bathroom multiple times the first night I carry the pager. I blame it on a bad bean burrito eaten around midnight but I know the truth deep down. Nerves combined with a mountain of ongoing learning and a nervous stomach. Bad combination.

The first time the code pager "goes off" while I'm carrying it, it;s 2:30 in the morning. Bee-bee-beeeeep. I nearly jump out of my skin. Adrenaline surges. I take a deep breath. My roiling stomach actually settles. My trembling hands stabilize. It turns out I'm calm in a real emergency, it's the imagined ones that wreak havoc.

I might save a life. I might do real CPR. I might save a life. It's time to make a difference!

I take off at a solid jog ready to do my part. *Let's do this.*

The code is over a half-mile from the ICU, about as far away as I can get from our unit. I don't go alone, my charge nurse comes with me. As I jog it never dawns on me, my charge nurse is walking. It never occurs to me, no one else is with us. I don't pause to consider, codes usually have a herd of people rushing there at the same time.

Doctors, nurses, pharmacists, respiratory therapists. A literal herd of people in scrubs.

When I arrive on the unit I am paged to I frantically look around for the action and noise. There's nothing going on. It's quiet. With codes there is noise and people and energy and equipment. But here, tonight, there is nothing. Everyone but the nursing staff is asleep.

The charge nurse, who's sitting at the main desk reading a book, just shakes his head. He flips off my charge nurse who comes walking up behind me. They know each other. My charge nurse laughs. I'm still anxiously looking around for where I can help. I am focused on saving a life.

I might save a life. I might do CPR. I might save a life...

My charge nurse finally has to spell it out for me.

Oh. I deflate. My face burns red. How embarrassing. Strangely enough though, my stomach is quiet the rest of the shift. I don't need Tums the next day or for many days after that.

The crew fake-pages me three more times before I get wise and stop jogging. I learn to wait for someone else to start moving before I get up and go. The fake pages stop. I continue carrying the code pager. Tums not needed.

After eight months the crew discovers I'm terrified of spiders. An irrational fear, but aren't most? Plastic spiders start showing up in my work pod. In my locker. On my water bottle. They are black, small, and plastic with long spindly legs. My heart races every time I see one. Once, I'm in the break room and see a spider behind the microwave. I grab it and throw it at the table towards the other nurses who are also on lunch break at 3:00 am. It turns out *that* spider was not fake. The spiders stop after that.

After two more months on the night shift I'm asked to help with a patient transfer. My charge nurse tells me a patient passed away at the change of shift. The body bag they put the patient in has a hole.

The deceased needs to be moved to a new bag. Something about poor quality control and the bags used to be thicker when he started. I try not to dwell on that much. They need one more person to help with the transfer. Fine. I walk into the room. There are three nurses on one side of the bed, me on the other.

"What the hell? Why am I alone on this side?" I ask, feeling irritable. I'm already behind for the night and want to catch up. "Let's just get this done."

I step up to the bed, ready to help. This is when the body bag, the white, plastic, hole-less bag that is lying inert on the bed, moves. The bag sits up. A roar comes from inside the bag.

I jump backwards and squat down on the floor, frantically looking side to side. *What the hell? Holy crap? What the hell?*

The other nurses laugh so hard some of them are crying. The nurse hiding in the bag is unzipped and reports it's hot in there. I watch as my colleagues help him out of the back. They also help me up off the floor, pat me on the back, and tell me I can be in the bag next time. I may be slightly gullible but there's no way they're getting me into one of those bags. *What if they don't unzip me?*

I'm deeply grateful today that cell phones did not exist then, in the same way they do now. None of this was filmed. And that was it. After that I am part of the crew.

No more pranks. Just a solid crew of nurses. None of the jokes, pranks, or fake codes ever interfered with really great patient care. No real codes were ever responded to slowly. No fake spiders were seen by patients (that I know of). No deceased patients were disrespected or handled poorly.

This may read like hazing but I never felt hazed. Perhaps it's because they played pranks on each other too. It was part of the culture on that unit. No one was immune to being the victim of a joke. If I ever have to be in an ICU as a patient I can only hope I wake up in an ICU with a crew of nurses that great.

They were tireless in their teaching. They made the mountain of learning scale. They had my back and each other's. To this day I believe they taught me more than I could ever repay them for. They shepherded me through the time when I knew (and feared) how much there was to be learned. When the canyon was so big it felt uncrossable.

They were my bridge, my rescue boat, my safe haven. It almost makes me want to go back in time and be a brand-new nurse again in that ICU... almost.

It wasn't until I needed to leave that job due to a move that I understood how important a strong team is. To really be a successful nurse (and survive in this business long term) I think you need a strong group of people around you. You won't always get along or like each other. But you will have each other's backs when the shit hits the fan, which it does in every type nursing job I've ever worked. At the end of the day, you do your job, but it's also your team who makes sure you're not left lying face down in the muck.

12

Shame.

Eileen is in her late-forties. She's currently living in the hospital on life-supporting medications. Waiting for a surgery and a miracle that will help extend her life. The first surgery will involve implanting a medical device that will buy her more time. Eileen is nervous about the device. There is a team in the hospital that helps manage the device. They're the experts. I'm not on that team.

I work as a nurse practitioner on a different hospital team that helps manage the life-supporting medications. Before daily rounds I check on Eileen. I listen to her heart and lungs. I check her ankles and her neck. I feel for pulses in her wrists and her feet. I ask her a few questions about pain, appetite, bowel movements, energy level. That's usually it. Today, though, Eileen has questions for me about the device. The device in which I am not an expert.

I try my best to answer her questions. It is not my area of expertise though.

In retrospect, I wish I hadn't tried. It would have saved everyone a lot of pain. The better option would have been to tell her "I don't manage that device, I'll let that team know you have questions." But that's not what I did, so here's the story.

Following our conversation, unbeknownst to me, Eileen complains to the head of my team. I scared her. She feels more uncertain about the device. She's not sure I gave her good information. She tells my attending doctor (the attending is the lead doctor for the team), I shouldn't be allowed to talk with people about things like this. She requests I be removed from her care team.

The complaint is shared with me by the attending doctor. During rounds. In front of the rest of the team. Matter-of-factly. Without warning.

After completing his verbal rundown of Eileen's complaint he states, "let the other team handle those questions. You should *not* be answering them. Don't answer questions you have no business answering. Now we have to reassign this patient because she doesn't want you anymore."

Weight settles on my shoulders. My face flushes. My hands tremble. I feel sick to my stomach.

I messed up. I failed. I created more work for other people. For my team. I shouldn't have tried. I thought I did my best. I failed. I'll make it right, somehow. Maybe I can fix it?

No one offers support. No one looks at me. Rounds continue.

This team is different. This mix of doctors, nurses, nurse practitioners, pharmacists. It's constantly changing. I don't know how to depend on. This isn't what I am used to. I need to harden up.

As the team talks about the next patient I am aware my hands are still trembling. The trembling in my hands is a new response for me. I don't know it yet, but I'll carry this with me for the rest of the time I have this job. It takes nearly two years for the trembling to start to fade away after I leave this job.

I'm aware of how much I have to learn to be good in this field. I'm aware of how ill the patients are. I'm aware of how much I cannot make any mistakes. Now on top of that, my baseline anxiety is piled high with shame, wrapped in guilt and delivered publicly in front of my so-called team.

I swear I tried my best. But I didn't know... That's not good enough here. How can I make it right? How can I make it better? I want to save lives. Help others.

But no one tells me it's alright. No one tells me I'll learn. No one tells me it will get better. No one steps in to help me learn. Everyone is too busy taking care of their own patients.

Later, I attempt to apologize to Eileen in her room (even though she asked me to not be on her care team again). I want to at least try.

"I'm sorry. I understand you felt scared and uncertain. My goal was to help. I truly didn't mean to make it worse. I know you're already in a scary situation. I should have told you I'd let the other team know you had questions. They could answer them. You don't need to feel worse. I'm sorry."

Eileen's eyes look blankly back at me. No anger. No kindness. No emotion at all. I look back and wait, expectantly. Hopeful. *I'm trying to fix this. To help my team. Maybe she'll give me a second chance.*

There is silence.

Then, Eileen's cell phone rings. I jump. She looks at the screen. Eileen answers the call. I stand there waiting. I'm uncertain if I should leave or wait. She laughs, responds, pauses. Her eyes sparkl-now e with life.

After what feels like an hour, but in reality is closer to three minutes, Eileen pauses. She looks at me. Her sparkling eyes go dead again.

"Oooh, you're still here. I don't need you. I asked for you to *not* be my provider again. You shouldn't be in my room."

Then she nods her head toward the door and points. She returns to her call, all life and laughter again. My anxious hands tremble in my pockets.

"Oh... that was just someone who needed to leave," I hear her say to the person on the other end of her call. Then she laughs again. A pause, as I walk around the curtain in front by the door. "Yeah, some people here are good. Some aren't. Some need to learn their place." Then more laughter.

I leave and close her door behind me.

Which one am I? I know I'm not good. Do I need to learn my place? Or am I simply not good?

My hands hide in my pockets, still shaking. More shame. More embarrassment. More guilt. I feel I could have done better. It seems obvious now. If I had known better, I could have done better. But how do I know without doing? Or without someone to teach me?

Finally, a flash of anger flares in my gut. I still have a little fight left. Otherwise I might as well be a pile of goo on the hospital floor. A big pile of nurse goo.

But then someone will have to clean up that mess too... More work for the environmental team. Clean up on ward 113. Spineless nurse practitioner on the floor. Unrecognizable pile of goo... use gloves, gown, and goggles. Proceed cautiously.

The anger keeps me afloat the rest of the day. It fuels my new mantra "I can do better." *I will do better. I will learn.*

But I also deserve better.

I carry this experience with me as a reminder of how important it is to say "I don't know" when I don't know something.

I don't know, but I'll find someone who does.

Or I'll figure it out and get back to you.

I don't know, yet. The 'yet' makes all the difference. *I don't know... yet. But I will find out.*

I don't have to hold all the answers (I never will).

I carry this experience with me as a reminder of how I choose to see and treat mistakes. Mistakes happen. They are part of being human. They're an opportunity to learn. To do better. To know better. They're a moment for growth. Mistakes are *not* an opportunity to tear someone down. To make them feel small. To belittle someone. Mistakes are a sign there is room for growth. Learn more, do better.

I carry this experience with me as a reminder of what it feels like to be part of a team (or not). A team is made of people who have my back. People who will stand up for me when I can't find my own words. People who will recognize a mistake and help me grow. People who are as human as I am. People who give grace to each other, not shame.

13

Clarification.

About ten years into my nursing career I became a nurse practitioner. The learning started all over again. For one of my jobs, as a nurse practitioner, I saw patients in a clinic for management of warfarin. Warfarin is an anticoagulant (a "blood thinner") and it requires a blood test for dosing. It is used to reduce the incidence of things like strokes, pulmonary emboli (blood clots in the lung), or venous blood clots.

A patient takes warfarin pills. Their blood is tested and a number is the result. There is a narrow goal range for that number. A variety of factors, which may interact with warfarin and affect that number, are reviewed. Then based on all of that information the warfarin dosing is adjusted individually for each patient.

One day I saw a patient and her number was really low. So low it was a completely normal number, as if she had no warfarin in her blood at all. This patient is at high risk for a stroke which is why she takes the medication in the first place. With a low number she is at her highest level of risk for stroke. She refuses to take the newer medications that don't require monitoring.

"I don't trust the new stuff," has been her response when I've tried to switch her over. Low numbers on warfarin can be due to not taking your warfarin, changes in your diet, medications, activity and so on. This visit went something like this...

"Your number is really low today. Did you possibly miss any doses of warfarin?" I ask Clarice.

"No. I didn't miss any doses. I take everything I'm supposed to take," Clarice replies briskly.

"Any changes in your diet or what you're eating?"

"No."

"Any changes in your medications, let's review your list..."

"No," she states both before and after we review her printed list of medications.

"Any new supplements, vitamins, herbals, or teas?"

"No."

"Any changes in your activity level? More walking? More exercise?" I ask, still hopeful we'll find an answer for this unexpected lab result.

"No."

"Any changes you can think of that would have caused your number to drop so much?"

"No..." Clarice pauses and looks at me.

"But I'm angry with my pharmacy. You," she points a long bony finger at my chest, "you ordered my warfarin two weeks ago. They never delivered it. Or called me. I'm mad about it."

"Umm, well let's look at that." I open up the computer in the room. We check on the order. "Yup, we ordered it two weeks ago and it went through, but you never received it?" *Something starts to tickle the back of my brain.*

"No," Clarice shakes her head at me. "I didn't."

"So did you miss any doses of warfarin?" I ask her again. *There's that tickle... What is it trying to tell me?*

"No. I already told you that," she snaps. She glares at me. *Oh, she's getting mad.*

I try again. "OK, yes. Did you... but did you... well, did you run out of warfarin?"

"Yes, one week ago when the new prescription didn't come," Clarice replies. *Ah-ha, that's the tickle.*

"OK, sooo... have you taken any warfarin this past week?" I ask tentatively, not sure what answer I am going to get. Not wanting to make her more mad but really wanting to get to the bottom of this.

"No. How would I do that?" she snaps. "I don't have any to take because it didn't get delivered. I told you this."

"Oh. Okay. But you didn't miss any doses?" I ask, giving this question one last try.

"What's wrong with you today? I already told you this. I did NOT miss any doses of warfarin." She glares at me again. *Yes, well, what is wrong with me today? Good question.*

"So just to clarify, you didn't take the warfarin for the past week because it was not delivered but you didn't miss any doses?"

"Yes." Clarice sits and glowers at me, lips tight, arms crossed. *I have not made a friend today.*

I kept asking Clarice if she missed any doses of warfarin. She kept telling me no. And getting angrier with me.

In her mind she hadn't missed any doses, despite not taking any. Sometimes it is hard to get clear answers to questions. What I've learned is sometimes it is hard to ask the right questions to get the information I need. Sometimes, despite years of experience, I'm back in a busy hospital hallway trying to get a partially dressed man back to his bed, uncertain of how to make progress. The man in the hallway wants one thing. I am focused on another.

Needless to say I followed up regarding her medication. It *had* been delivered by the pharmacy over a week ago. After going home she later found it tucked behind something on her kitchen counter. She resumed taking the medication. When she returned to clinic three days later her blood check was fine. It turns out when you take your medication it often works better, than when you don't.

14

Cultural incompetence.

When I worked in hospice I was frequently confronted by a certain situation. Family or friends of the patient didn't want me to say I worked with hospice. Or talk about death. Don't tell the patient you're a hospice nurse. You can be a visiting nurse, Dr. So-and-so's nurse, a consultant nurse, but *not* a hospice nurse.

There have been many different reasons for people asking me to say I am something other than what I am. It seems the most common reasons are related to fear and culture.

A nurse mentor, who'd been doing hospice work much longer than I, advised me early on, don't lie. Tell the truth. Let families know upfront you will not volunteer the information. However if the patient brings it up, you won't lie to them. I liked this. I followed her recommendation.

I let families and friends know, right in the beginning, I will not be deceptive about what I do. Yes, I can say I'm a visiting nurse or a consultant or whatever you want to call me. But if my patient asks, if I work for hospice, I will tell my patient the truth. If my patient asks me about death, I will talk about it. I try to make sure people know this before I walk in the door.

What I've found in practice is nearly every patient already knows. They know regardless of whether or not I tell them. They know regardless of what their family or friends want them to know.

After one or two visits, when the patient is more comfortable with me, they'll often slip a question into the conversation to confirm what they already suspect. The question might be something like, "you're a visiting nurse but this is hospice, right?" Sometimes it's more confrontational, like "why do you call yourself a visiting nurse when you really work for hospice?"

After the patient has asked their question, and the truth has been confirmed, it opens up opportunities to talk. (Usually.) To talk about why hospice is there. About what hospice is and isn't. To talk about the additional support services hospice may be able to offer. To prepare for the impossible, unpreparable, inevitable.

When I reflect back on this challenge, of being a hospice nurse who is asked to not use the words hospice or death, one encounter still comes to mind.

Joyce is the patient. Greta is her daughter. They live together in a quiet, modest home. Both had lost their husbands when they were young. They moved in together and aged together. Mother and daughter.

Most communication goes through Greta. Greta is adamant I say nothing about hospice, death, or dying. This goes beyond not saying I'm a hospice nurse. This includes all forms of the words death, dying, end-of-life, hospice, or anything else equivalent.

At each visit Greta welcomes me into the home. Then she reminds me, "You are not to use the words death, or dying, or hospice in any way, when you talk with my mom. She can't handle it. We do not discuss death in our culture."

At each visit I nod and explain to Greta, "I won't bring these words up. But if your mother asks me about these words or if I work for hospice I will respond truthfully."

It feels like a strange game of chicken. Who will say the D-word first? Me? Her mom? Greta?

This goes on for at least two months. I am mildly surprised Greta does not hand me a list of forbidden words each time I visit their home. *Perhaps a laminated copy would be helpful? It could be wiped down after each visit and reused?*

In the first two months Joyce doesn't ask me anything about death, dying, or hospice. My visits are uneventful. Despite insisting I not speak certain words, Greta does not come into the room for the visits. She says she respects her mother's privacy. Greta asks me for a brief report when I leave, otherwise she is not involved in the visit. I usually talk with Greta about changes to medications, appetite, bowel habits, or skin issues. We do not talk about death.

Then one day this changes.

As I am listening to Joyce's abdomen she starts talking.

"I don't feel like eating. Nothing tastes good. Nothing smells right. I don't eat much," she repeats. She looks at me. I nod.

"Unless Greta's watching me. She works hard to cook good food... It's nice... But I'm not eating much..." she pauses, it seems, to make sure she has my full attention. I remove my stethoscope and stop what I am doing to hear what she has to say. I sense this is going somewhere.

Joyce resumes, "So I'm not eating. I'm losing weight. It doesn't really bother me..." Joyce stops and looks around, then simply says, "I think I'm dying." She looks at me. It's quiet, deadly quiet, in the room. I blink. And swallow. *She said dying. Oh crap.*

I wait for the "death police" to rush the room. Joyce just used the D-word. I blink and pause, trying to figure out what to do. I try not to meet her eyes.

How do I do this? How do I avoid this? Look at the plants. Look at the floor. Look at the blanket. Look anywhere but at Joyce...

"Am I dying?" Joyce asks me quietly. Her deep brown eyes are clear and focused on mine.

Could someone please zap me somewhere? Anywhere. Big hole in the ground? Big earthquake? Anything to get me out of here? Oh man, Greta is going to be mad.

I can't ignore this question. Yet I don't know what to say.

Normally, I'd simply say "yes". Yes, this might be a change that happens near the end of life. Yes, let's talk about it. Yes, what do you think this means?

But I'm not supposed to do any of that.

How do I answer her question about dying?

How do I honor the wishes of her daughter and respect their culture, which *does not* talk about dying?

I don't know how to do this. If I don't answer this question for Joyce, who will? Isn't this my job? Isn't this why I'm here?

I sigh and pick a side. Knowing what I say next will have repercussions.

"Joyce, you might be starting the process. It's hard to say for certain. The body shuts down, slowly. I don't think you're actively dying. These changes you're noticing may be part of a process that takes time. It starts to happen as you approach the end of your life."

She nods. "I thought it might be so," she says. Then she pats my arm and closes her deep brown eyes. It is the end of our conversation.

I do not mention the conversation to Greta when I leave. In retrospect this was probably a mistake, but, I was afraid.

Two hours later I'm at a different house when my pager buzzes. My office is paging me "stat," asking me to call immediately. I never get paged "stat." Tendrils of worry start to creep into my gut. *This has to do with Joyce. Did something happen to Joyce because we talked about death? Could she really not handle it? Did she die? Oh no...*

I call the office and some of my suspicions are confirmed. This is about Joyce. But Joyce is alive. Greta is furious. I talked about death with her mother. She is consulting a lawyer and threatening to sue. I have not provided culturally competent care for her mother.

I finish my visits for the day and return to the main office. I'm brought into a room and the door is closed. Never a good sign. My manager tells me about the complaints leveled against me and the hospice.

"Did you use the word dying? Did you talk about end of life with this patient?" she asks me.

"Yes," I answer. *I knew there would be repercussions. What would have happened if I had told Greta before I left?*

"Did you know Greta didn't want you to use the words death or dying due to their cultural beliefs?" she asks me.

"Yes... but I also told Greta I'd answer Joyce honestly if she asked me about death or dying or hospice. I would not bring it up. I *didn't* bring it up. But I would talk about it, if Joyce brought it up. She did. She asked me."

My manager shakes her head and sighs, "so you told Greta you would disobey their request to honor their cultural beliefs? You knew what they did *not* want? You did it *anyway?*"

"Yes. But... well, when you put it like that..." I trail off. Heavy silence hangs in the room. The worry that started as tendrils in my gut has grown into large, choking roots. There is something I want to say but I can't quite figure out what it is. *Something else I need to say... There's another important piece to this. What is it?*

My manager breaks the silence. "Okay. So this case will be re-assigned..." She looks at her computer and does not speak again. Tap. Tap. Tap.

My gut's in knots. There's something I'm missing. Something I need to say. *What is it? What am I missing?*

"What would you have done?" I ask my manager. "What would you have done if a ninety-five year old woman with end-stage heart failure asks you about changes in eating? And weight loss? What would you say, if she asks you if she's dying?"

"I would have honored their wishes," says my manager. End of story. *But...*

I failed in providing culturally competent care as it was defined. While I didn't bring up death, it was still my responsibility to not talk about death. My manager did the only thing she could. I was removed from the case and someone who could be more culturally competent replaced me. I was signed up for cultural competency training.

Five weeks later Joyce passed away.

To this day I struggle with whether or not I truly did something wrong. *Perhaps there can be more than one right answer?* I am aware I did not provide culturally competent care as it was defined by Greta. I talked about dying with a woman whose culture did not allow her to discuss death. *But...*

But... But if that woman is part of a culture that does not speak about death or dying, then why is that woman asking me about dying? Why is Joyce asking me how long until she dies? And who else would answer her question, if not me, a nurse from hospice?

15

I don't know.

I didn't ask the question I should have asked. In retrospect, I wish I had asked it. The thing about retrospect, though, is it happens *afterwards*. Now I can only soldier onward with my hard won, painful knowledge, lodged deep in my gut, like a piece of shrapnel.

I remain uncertain, years later, if it would have made any difference to ask the question. Despite reassurances to the contrary, I still wonder.

Hannah is young, early sixties. She has been dealt bad genetic hands in her heart, lungs, and kidneys. All of them failing at the same time. Her medications are optimized. All seventeen of them, taken multiple times a day. This list of seventeen doesn't even include the twelve she can take as needed. Twenty-nine different prescriptions once you add them up.

But Hannah is alive.

Hannah is on supplemental oxygen 100% of the time due to her lungs. She wears a mask over her nose and mouth or two small tubes in her nose when eating. She eats quickly because her oxygen level drops perilously low when she isn't wearing the mask.

She can leave her house if she has three people helping her. So much equipment to move. To walk. To go anywhere beyond the four walls she calls home. Hannah, her medications, her oxygen, all perfectly balanced, on a tightrope, so high up. But with no safety net. And a fatally long way to fall.

Hannah chooses to start hospice when the prognoses from her Pulmonologist, Cardiologist, and Nephrologist were all six months or less. Six months (or less) of life left to live. We meet late on a Friday afternoon to discuss hospice services and sign papers.

Hannah is polite, listening attentively to everything I have to say about hospice. Her husband sits quietly by her side. He nods. Holds her hand. They are both stoic and composed. *Where is the emotion,* I wonder. *This woman, this young woman, is starting hospice. It's not fair. Life is not fair. Where is the rage? Is this what years of living with chronic illness do to you?*

I can still picture this quiet couple seated on their beige couch in their clean, stark apartment. Beige carpet, beige walls, beige artwork. Her small, bird-like body looks as if she is being swallowed by beige. *Has her life always been beige? Did that come with the illnesses? Are there any other colors in the apartment? In their life?* Can I look around your apartment, I want to ask. But I don't. We focus on paperwork and healthcare.

I complete my physical exam. Paperwork is signed. A follow up visit is scheduled for Monday. I am packed and leaving when Hannah asks her question.

"What if I stop taking all my medications? What will happen?" she asks. Her voice is calm and clear. No hesitancy.

I pause. Think. Answer as truthfully as I can, knowing there is no way to answer this question.

"I don't know, but you would most likely die..." I tell her. "Although maybe not. It's impossible to predict something like that."

Death might happen? Or not? I'm not sure.

"Each of your medications keeps your body functioning as well as we can hope for. It's all a balancing act. You have a very good team of doctors and practitioners." I nod and smile, as if this makes it better. I think I am being reassuring. She does have excellent doctors.

"How long would it take to die?" Her next question is another one I cannot answer. I feel twitchy, like I need to move.

Why am I uncomfortable?

"I don't know," I respond. "Everyone has a different process when dying. It's unpredictable." *Dying is unpredictable, unique to each person.*

"But if you had to guess... how long?" she presses me. Internally I step back. I feel cornered. Scared. This is not how hospice intakes usually go. People usually want to know more about the living, not the dying. They want to know how to get more time.

I answer her again, "I don't know how long it would take. Twenty-four to forty-eight hours? Possibly less? Maybe more? No one can predict that." *I don't know. Run. Move. Twitch. Run. It is not supposed to go like this.*

Uncomfortable grows and swirls around me. It rustles my hair and my heart beats faster.

"Will it hurt?" Hannah asks me. Then she clarifies, "will the dying hurt?"

Her husband sits, holding her hand on the couch. They both look interested to hear the answer to yet *another* question I can't answer. They look as if we're discussing something like golf or the weather, not death. They're watching me, waiting.

Their houes is nearly silent. The oxygen machine whooshes in and out as Hannah breathes. Sniff puff. Sniff puff. A faint hum in the background. My desire to run ratchets up with every sniff-puff of the oxygen machine. Every question I can't answer.

"Umm, I don't know that either. No one does. Will it hurt? Pain? Possibly." I pause again.

I am deeply aware I keep saying "I don't know." I wonder if this ever gets easier. *I don't know. No one knows.*

I like having answers. I have been working in hospice for over a year and try to provide answers. But today it is all, "I don't know. I don't know," for every answer. These questions don't have solid answers. Because every person, every death is different.

I don't know.

I hear alarm bells in my head. Feel my heart pounding in my chest. *Lub-dub. Don't-know. Lub-dub. Don't-know.* The urge to run is growing.

Something is not right.

"Why?" I finally ask Hannah, "Why do you want to know... all of this?" I flap my hands trying to encompass the gravity of this conversation.

"Just curious," she responds, shrugging her shoulders. I nod. But it feels unfinished. There is something more to say, but I don't know what it is. *What am I supposed to say? Ask? I don't know.*

Then the visit is done. Our first follow up appointment is scheduled for Monday. Hannah's husband shows me to the door. Hannah sits on the beige couch and watches me leave. Sniff puff. Hum. Sniff puff. Hum. *What am I not asking? I don't know...*

I met Hannah on a Friday night, when she started hospice services. Hannah stopped all her medications Saturday night. She died on Sunday, very early in the morning.

I wasn't there. Another nurse was on call. She said it was very peaceful, very quick. The nurse said everything was already arranged. Funeral home. Family had been called. She said it was the smoothest death she had attended.

Can there be such a thing as a smooth death? I don't know. Or, I did not know before this, but now I do.

Now, I also know, to ask all the questions. Keep asking until I know I have done all I can. When my hair swirls and pain grows and I want to run, I stop and ask. When my muscles twitch and I feel tense and uncertain, I stop and ask.

Are you thinking about stopping all your medications?

Are you thinking about ending your life?

Are you suicidal?

Do you have a plan?

Let me find help for you.

We'll work together and find you help. I don't have the answers but we'll find help.

I wish I'd known to ask those questions, to say those things. But as I wrote at the beginning, I don't know if it would've made a difference for Hannah.

What I do know, is it would've made a difference for me.

***

"Starting out" is what these stories have been about. The beginning of something new is often talked about as exciting and fresh. Yet it may also be scary or uncertain. It's an interesting place to be in. Unsure, excited, nervous, hopeful. Despite having been a nurse for decades now, I'm still surprised by how often "starting out days" happen .

The stories I've shared so far are about lives entering the world and leaving the world. There are dentures. There are books and the realization that books and real life don't always match up. There's being a part of a team and feeling unwelcome. And there are mistakes and trying to apologize for those mistakes. There's a lot of learning about how and when to ask questions and what questions to ask.

When we're starting out, may we all give ourselves a little more grace, a little more tenderness, knowing that doing something new is often uncomfortable but it's the only way to get better. It's also part of this profession in nursing. Since nursing is constantly changing and growing and evolving, so must we. To be truly successful as a nurse it's important to embrace this idea of constant growth early on. Be ready to learn, grow, and have your practice change, and you will be one step closer to having a successful nursing career.

Growing

" Be not afraid of growing slowly,
be only afraid of standing still. "

- Chinese proverb

16

Hope.

Brendon is not my regular patient but I squeeze him into my schedule. Cross covering is not unusual and often required in a clinic that manages high risk medications. Brendon enters the exam room. He doesn't sit. I feel compelled to stand. To match him. My hands shake slightly, a nervous tic I acquired from a previous job. My shaking hands have slowly improved but sometimes flare up when I'm nervous. In this exam room with this man today, I'm nervous. *Why?*

I efficiently see to the healthcare business Brendon came to the clinic for. It goes quickly. *Why am I so nervous?* My hands are just starting to settle when he asks a question. *The* question. Or *one* of *the* questions that gets my attention.

"What happens if I take all this medication at once?" he asks me. As if he's only just now thought of this question.

"Nothing good," I respond without much thought. Then pause. My hair tingles. My heart beats faster. My hands shake more. I have been here before. I have learned to listen to my hands and hair.

Are you alright? Are you safe? Are you thinking about taking all that medication? Do you need help? Are you considering suicide? Do you have a plan? I hate asking these questions.

But I hate *not* asking them more.

I look at this man who still isn't seated. This man I don't know very well. I take a deep breath and summon strength. Resolve. I flashback to a beige room and a woman asking me what happens if she stops all her medications. *Ask the questions.*

"Brendon, are you alright?"

"Yes," he says. No emotion.

"Are you safe?"

"Yes."

"Are you thinking about taking all that medication?"

"No." He does not pause, but he also does not meet my eyes.

"Do you need help?"

"No."

"Are you considering suicide?"

"No."

"Do you have a plan?"

"No." He has passed the test.

All the "right" things are spoken. My hands shake. My gut twists. Some of the answers are lies. The room is too hot.

Brendon continues standing in the small exam room. *Why doesn't he walk out the door? Why is he putting up with my questions?* The healthcare is done. He's done what he technically came for. And yet... *he is still here.*

Brendon looks at me with no emotion. I try again.

I ask him, "are you truly alright? If you're not alright I can help. We can find help. Together." My shaking hands calm a little.

This is the question I need to ask. The path I need to walk. How else can I ask this? My gut doesn't believe his answers.

Brendon finally fidgets, his right hand plays with a loose zipper on his jacket. He studies the enlarged picture of a cactus on the matte blue accent wall in the exam room. He doesn't speak. I smell the faint hint of his cologne mixed with the antiseptic odor of the medical room. Time stretches. *Will he open up? Will he talk?* Then a loud crash rattles the hallway outside my exam room. We both jump. I yelp a little.

"I'm alright, thank you for seeing me." Brendon leaves.

I can't detain him. I can't chase him to his car and ask him again. *Are you really alright? Really?* But my gut is telling me I need to do something. My trembling hands agree.

There are three more patients lined up, ready to be seen. Toes tapping. Eyes watching. Phones being scanned but not patiently. These patients, they are not patient. They know my last patient just left. The room is empty. It's someone else's turn.

Stay on time? See my next patient? Do something else for Brendon?

I close my exam room door. *Do something else.* I look at Brendon's chart. I decide to call someone who hopefully knows him better than me. I have met Brendon *once*. Today only. Yet my gut tells me something is not right.

I call his primary care doctor (PCP) but can only leave a message on a private voicemail. It feels so inadequate. I try to explain all of it in less than ninety seconds. I'm concerned. This visit didn't feel right. I hope you know this man better than me. Can you follow up? I try to explain my shaking hands and tingling hair. To the empty abyss that is voicemail. *Will anyone listen to this? Will they do anything? Will it help?*

Then, my day continues. There are now four impatient patients waiting. I am behind for the rest of the day. There are six hours left. I apologize to each poorly veiled comment about having to wait so long.

"Yes, I know you had to wait. I'm sorry your day did not go as planned or scheduled," I reply, meaning it.

My day hasn't gone as planned either. I'm worried about a man I never met until today. I'm worried he's going to take his own life. I'm behind because I decided to do something about it. To try... But I never say this part out loud. I simply apologize and continue the business of healthcare.

I wonder. *Did anyone get my message? Is the private voicemail actually checked? Will anyone follow up? Will he live?*

Eight weeks go by. Brendon doesn't return to the clinic. He's overdue for follow-up. He can't be reached by phone or mail.

When I think about Brendon my gut insists loudly, "we were right." *We were right. I don't want to be right.*

Then one afternoon, nine weeks later, Brendon is in the lobby. No appointment scheduled. Insisting loudly he needs to see me. Only me. I can hear him down the hall from my exam room.

I cringe.

Is he mad? Does he know I called his primary care doctor and asked her to follow up? Does he know I expressed concerns despite him telling me all the "right" answers? Does he know I thought he was considering suicide? Of course he knows. Yet, I think I did the right thing. I think, but I'm not certain.

Brendon is ushered back to my exam room and deemed my problem now by the front office staff. He cuts the line. There will be more apologies today. I can see the impatient phone watchers looking at me as this man is escorted into my exam room.

Brendon and I are in the exam room with the cactus picture again. He looks at the blue wall. He looks at me. My hands have started shaking again. I stuff them in my pockets.

Brendon sits down this time. It catches me by surprise.

I sit so quickly I almost miss my chair.

Brendon looks at me and simply says, "thank you."

Thank you? He reads my puzzled expression and explains. He was not alright the day I saw him, eight weeks ago.

He was going to take his medication. All of it. He was planning to commit suicide.

His primary care doctor called him. She talked with him. They found help. He got the help he needed.

"Thank you," he says again.

"You're welcome," I say back. Finally able to talk. My hair and hands are quiet.

I'm starting to realize there's a lot more to healthcare than health and care. Sometimes I'm able to provide something more than the business end of healthcare. I'm able to provide the care someone is actually seeking. It's one of the reasons I became a nurse to begin with, to care for people.

It isn't easy to ask someone if they're thinking about suicide. Despite having asked these questions (many times), it doesn't get easier (at least it hasn't for me). When I started in nursing there was no training for how to ask these questions or what to do next. There was less awareness. It's still not easy to know what to do if someone says yes.

But fumbling through the asking and flailing through the getting help is exponentially better than not asking at all. Make phone calls. Find a hotline, use it. Seek a reputable place to get help on the internet and call them or go there. Contact someone who knows what to do. Go to the ER.

Having lived through both, I would rather live with the discomfort of asking the questions and doing too much. Then live through the pain of not asking the questions and doing too little. Even in the darkest hour, there is always hope.

17

The unanswerable question.

"Should I get married?" Tracy asks as we step outside the room at the skilled nursing facility. "Should I do it now? Should I wait?"

"Ermm," I falter, feeling utterly unprepared to answer this question. "Well, that's up to you...." I don't know what to tell her. As a hospice nurse this isn't my question. I'm far more comfortable being asked questions about death and dying, not about getting married and when. Yett I know how we ended up here. I just don't have an answer for her.

Tracy's wedding is scheduled for tomorrow. Her mother, Marilyn, has been in a skilled nursing facility for the past year for a variety of health issues and overall decline. Tracy, the woman standing across from me in the busy hallway, is middle aged and getting married for the first time. Family has been coming into town for the previous five days. Getting ready for Tracy's wedding. Coming to say hello to Marilyn, mother of the bride. Say goodbye too, as it turns out. It *isn't* supposed to be this way. It never is. But sometimes, life has terrible timing and disregards all plans.

Marilyn is relatively young to be in a skilled nursing facility. A perfect storm of diagnoses all hit at the same time leading to an inability to care for herself, fully remember herself or thrive. Tracy told me Marilyn wrestled and struggled against it. She fought against the diseases, the decline, the painful inevitability of it all.

After losing Marilyn for 24 hours, she was found wandering in a canyon by joggers the next day, the decision was made to move Marilyn to a twenty-four-hour managed care facility. Tracy helped Marilyn move from the house she had grown up in, to the four walls she occupies now. And thus Marilyn has slowly declined here for the past year. Hospice was ordered about four months ago when the decline became more rapid. This is when I met them.

About the same time Tracy was moving her mom into a skilled nursing facility, she met a man. They fell in love. They got engaged. They planned a wedding.

Marilyn is happy for Tracy. She's happy when she remembers who Tracy is and what she's supposed to be happy about. Some days both are a little murky.

Up until the week before the wedding Tracy and I have been trying to figure out how to safely transport Marilyn to the wedding then back to the skilled nursing facility. She's well enough to sit up and leave the facility in a wheelchair with a caregiver for a short time. We aren't sure how long she can be out, but we're hoping to get her through the ceremony and the first half-hour of the reception. But this final decline, the one that started four days ago, was so sudden, unexpected, and quick. No one was really prepared for it. Despite working in hospice, I wasn't prepared for it. We were so focused on getting Marilyn to the wedding.

"What's a wedding?" Marilyn asked me a week ago when I stopped by to check on her. It was a murky day. "Everyone keeps asking me about the wedding," she confides, "but I don't know what that is...." She whispers this to me as I lean in to listen to her lungs with my stethoscope.

"Oh gosh," is all I can think to say at that moment, to the mother of the bride. *Oh gosh. Life is messy.*

"Well Marilyn, a wedding is when two people get married..." I try to explain as I sit on the edge of her bed. She nods along, listening to me.

Now, after seeing all the family and friends in the past five days, Marilyn stopped waking up. Stopped talking. Stopped eating. Stopped drinking. Stopped responding most of the time. She smiles at voices but doesn't change or move otherwise. She's breathing. She has a pulse. But no food and no water for two days.

Now, here is this question, from Tracy, "should I get married? Tomorrow? All these people are here. Everything planned. Planned for the past year..."

So we both stand in the hallway. Her looking at me with her unanswerable question and some sort of hope I will have an answer. But I have no answer. I am painfully aware I don't know how to answer this question or what to even say to this woman. Aside from, "I'm so sorry." I'm so sorry this is happening right before your wedding. We'll do our best to keep your mom comfortable, which is what she wanted. I'm so sorry.

Yet really, the question is not "should I get married?" The real question is, "will my mom die tomorrow? Will my mom die on my wedding day? And what do I do?"

"I don't know," is all I can say. Because the truth is, I don't know how to answer this question. No one does. And I accept that I do not (and never will) hold all the answers. No one will. The best we can do, as nurses (or humans) is to remember to be kind, graceful, and grateful for the time we are given. Be grateful for the lessons we may learn throughout this journey we call life.

18

Running.

I am running, running, running. Down the hallway in a large hospital. I navigate a maze of hallways wearing my blue, hospital-issued scrubs and my trusty (but ancient) running shoes. My heart rate sky-rockets. It has nothing to do with the running. It has everything to do with my pager, which beeps again and again. I run faster.

My scrubs are standard-issued and faded light blue, like those worn in so many hospitals. When they get wet anyone can see they're wet because the light blue instantly becomes dark. There are two wet spots on my chest, dripping on the soft blue fabric. I run faster. Aware of the spectacle I am making.

People turn in their chairs or work pods to watch, alert to the fact someone is running. Do they need to run too? I feel embarrassed. My face is red and uncomfortably warm. My pager beeps again and again.

My life feels like it's unraveling with each beep. With each beep I wonder more and more, how long will it take my life to unravel? And while my life feels as if it is unraveling, is someone else's life ending? I hope not.

How did I get here? It was not supposed to be like this. Never like this.

I gave birth to a baby ten weeks ago. A healthy baby girl who started day care last week. I'm back at work, my physical scars mostly healed. The emotional scars from a traumatic delivery, less healed. I'm trying (desperately) to save people, help people, and be part of a team. I'm trying to be a mom to a newborn and a preschooler. To be a wife. To hold onto my sanity. Yet it feels like everything is slipping, slippery, too hard to hold onto it all. *How did I get here? Running down this hall?* My chest, wet with breast milk, dripping down my scrubs. There was no time to slip the pads back into the nursing bra I wear beneath my light-blue hospital-issued scrubs.

I work as a nurse practitioner in a large hospital. I'm part of a team that takes care of patients who are extremely ill. Close to death but not dying, we hope. Many of them are waiting for a miracle to arrive. My team includes doctors, fellows, interns, residents, pharmacists, social workers, and nurse practitioners. I'm trying to be part of this team but I don't seem to fit anywhere.

I have nowhere to sit. Nowhere to store my bag each day. Nowhere to eat my lunch. Nowhere to store a few books to refer to if I need help. Similar to my scrubs not fitting quite right when I returned to work. I'm aware of not belonging in the same way these scrubs are too tight across my hips and my belly.

Despite returning to work, I am still breastfeeding by ten-week-old baby girl. I understand, from the pediatrician, my obstetrician, and the moms group, I am supposed to do this for her health and mine. Somehow I'm supposed to be able to pump throughout the work day so I can continue to breastfeed at home too. Somehow I am supposed to find the time in the day to drop everything, find a space to pump, actually relax, pump, and return to work. "Breast-is-best" is plastered throughout the inside of my brain. I'm not so sure anymore... one week and this is not working. This worked, before I went back to work. But not now.

At my work there's a closet, many units and hallways away from where I do my work in the hospital. The closet contains a working outlet, a partially broken chair, and a few ancient People magazines. I understand I'm supposed to be grateful for this closet. (I suppose I am, it's better than the bathroom floor.) When I need to pump, I dash to the closet with my bag of equipment. I'm allotted twenty total minutes of time by my team to do this. That twenty minutes includes getting to the closet, setting up, pumping, cleaning up, and getting back to work. Anyone who has tried to pump breast milk realizes the futility of this.

While I pump, someone else on the team covers my patients. The others on my team already have their own load of patients. Those who have to cover are not especially kind or understanding about the process. In a twelve-hour shift I will most likely need to pump twice. It's more work for them, my team. I'm aware of this.

Today, "the other," who's covering my patients while I take a "pump break," tells me he won't do it. Will not. He didn't sign up for this. For watching my patients so I can take extra breaks during the day. This is during rounds in front of the entire team.

What team? This isn't my team? How did this become my life? I can't do this...

"If something happens while you're pumping, well, that's on you," he says after stating he won't do it. No one else says anything. No one on the team speaks up. I don't speak up either. I don't defend myself.

Why am I not speaking up? This isn't me. How'd I become this person who doesn't speak up for what I believe to be right? I don't even speak up for myself?

Following rounds "the other" quietly tells me, where no one else can here "I'm not responsible for your inability to do your job. You decide what's more important. Saving lives or breast milk."

My gut twists. My pulse races. My mind seethes. I can't seem to form a comeback. Possibly due to ten weeks of sleep deprivation, hormones, or stress. Before the birth of my daughter I already felt deeply incompetent. Unprepared for this job I'm supposed to be doing. Trying to do.

I'm aware of how much I don't know. How much I need to learn. How high the stakes are. "The other's" comments are not helping. Being a new mom is not helping. Pumping breast milk is not helping. *I want to be good at this job. But I also want to be a good mom. I want to do both...*

Now, thirty minutes after that conversation with "the other," I'm running down a hall. I made my choice. I chose breast milk and my ten-week old daughter.

I am running, running, running. My scrubs are wet with breast milk. My pumping equipment is haphazardly thrown into a bag. The suction devices flop back and forth for anyone to see as I jog through the maze of hallways to my patient who is coding. My patient. This is the patient "the other" said he would not cover. *Is he covering? Surely someone will have done something? Surely someone is saving this life... I hope...*

Shame. Humiliation. Guilt. Fear. They slosh around me like the scant amount of breast milk in the bottles. The scant amount I was able to collect. Before I am paged back to the reality of my crumbling life. *What am I going to do? I do not belong here. I cannot sustain this. This is unsustainable.*

I arrive at the hallway of the patient. I can already tell the room is filled to capacity. Everyone doing their jobs. Everyone except me. The attending doctor is running the code, as generally happens.

"The other" stands at the door looking in. He turns as he hears me coming down the hall. Slap, slosh. Slap, slosh. Slap, slosh.

Despite knowing I'm not needed, I run the rest of the way to the room. I halt. "The other" is gatekeeping.

He looks at my chest, my open bag of equipment, my pride. He grimaces, like he's seeing something awful, something he wishes he didn't have to see.

How did I get here? How do I get out? Is there an out? No. This is the state of early-days motherhood in the USA if you want a child and a job. This is what you're looking at. Work-life balance? I think not.

"You are not needed," the other says to me. Four words. Then he returns his attention to the room where the saving of a life continues in earnest. I'm left looking at his white-coated back and crisp clean blue scrubs.

What would happen if I poured my breast milk on your jacket and quit? Right now?

But I deliver no comeback. No witty retort. I turn and walk away. I decide not to waste my breast milk on his back. Walk, slosh. Walk, slosh. Walk, slosh.

I am walking, walking, walking, head down. I don't belong here. I am not part of this team. I am not needed in that room. I cannot go back to the pump room. I am lost.

I ask the nurses at the main station for new scrubs. They say they can't give me any. I'm not on the nursing staff. I'm considered medical staff. It'll mess up their numbers. I can go to the medical laundry in the bowels of the building and ask for fresh scrubs.

For God's sakes?!? Look at me. Someone look at me. What's happened to the caring in healthcare? I need clean scrubs. I'm a nurse, but I can't get clean scrubs at the nurse's station because I'm a nurse practitioner now. I fit nowhere, including in my scrubs. I want to scream. To quit. To give up.

I consider the maze of hallways and stairwells to get to the medical laundry. It doesn't feel worth it to drag my humiliation with me through more of the hospital. I dig my jacket out of my backpack that's hiding on the floor behind a trashcan because there is nowhere to store my stuff. I wipe off my chest and scrubs as best I can. I tuck pads back into the nursing bra. I wear the jacket for the rest of my shift.

I chose breast milk. And then my patient coded. At the same time. Did I make the wrong choice? Beyond the embarrassment, guilt, loneliness. Beyond all that, in my gut, I feel alright.

I chose right. It starts to burn like kindling for a fire somewhere deep inside of me. *I chose what is right for me. For my family. For who I am. For who I want to be. For who I am becoming.*

The code continues. The patient (my patient) is stabilized and saved. The business of healthcare carries on. Later I try to talk with the attending doctor. I try to explain, to ask how I can do this differently. How can I pump and take care of patients? How can I have both, my family and a career in healthcare? My 10-week old daughter and saving lives? How can I balance all of this? Is there balance?

He tells me to, "work it out with the rest of the team." It's not his problem." That's it.

Ha. What team? I wonder. *I am not part of a team. Not this team.*

I give my notice days later. I can't be a member of this team in the way the team needs me to be a member. I know how much I would have to give up to become competent in this world of life saving. Aware, in my gut, I am not willing to make the sacrifices needed to do this job.

I choose my daughter, my preschooler, my marriage. I choose my family. I will find a different path. I choose to find myself and not be lost to this team and it's rigorous demands. The demands are rigorous for a reason - these patients are really ill. They deserve the best. I cannot give them that.

I am running, running, running away. But I believe I am also running, running, running to something better.

There will be nursing jobs we know we *can do*, but the cost will be high. Sometimes the cost is worth it. It's worth it to give one-hundred-percent of what you've got to the job, the team, the lives that will be saved. And yet sometimes it's also worth it to walk away and find something else that allows you to give a percentage to work and another percentage to home or family or self or friends or something else. It's alright to give it all. But it's also alright to recognize when you need to be a nurse and have balance beyond that too.

19

Let him talk.

Amos comes to the outpatient clinic for routine check-ups. He has a laundry list of ailments and another list of medications and supplements he takes for those ailments. He is usually transported to and from the clinic by a caregiver. Amos comes into his visits alone though. About a year ago he added a wheelchair to his routine following an eighth fall with an eighth trip to the emergency room in so many weeks. He is very lucky none of those falls resulted in catastrophic injuries.

"A cat," Amos once told me. "I'm a cat. I have used my eight lives. Now I need a wheelchair for the ninth."

One of Amos' ailments affected his ability to speak. He can speak but it's garbled and mixed. It takes time for him to form the words and get them into the world. Sometimes the words are like alphabet soup. He puts them back in the bowl, rearranges them and tries again. Sometimes I write the words down to clarify. He nods yes or no in answer. We work our way through each visit. It takes time. It takes patience. I do not mind. I look forward to my visits with Amos.

One day he arrives to the clinic with his caregiver. And his wife.

In all the years I have been seeing Amos I haven't previously met his wife. We've spoken on the phone numerous times. She manages the two-page laundry list of medications, making sure he takes them all on time. She checks his skin for sores. Schedules appointments for all his specialists. Makes sure he doesn't miss one. She manages his healthcare with precision. She's been lovely to talk with on the phone. She knows exactly what's happening at all times. Amos is healthier, more viable, with far fewer complications, than many others would be in his position. I believe a lot of that is due to his wife.

On this day, when they both come in for the visit, I introduce myself. We get down to business. There is much to cover in twenty minutes but we usually get through it, Amos and I.

I ask Amos how he's been feeling after an adjustment we made a month ago. He looks at me and starts to speak, one word, then the next, slowly. Deliberately. His words take time. His wife launches in over his third word and answers my question. Her answer is exactly the information I need, clinically. *Healthcare.*

I ask Amos another question, this time about his appetite to determine if there are any changes. He starts again, word salad this time. Pauses. Starts over. His wife tells me he isn't eating as much. Some changes in taste. He lost a few pounds. She's adding a protein supplement every other day. She is clear and accurate. Her answer is exactly what I need clinically. *Healthcare.*

Amos looks down. I feel the first twinges of irritation. *Deep breath. Refocus. It's good to have the information I need.*

I look at Amos again, this time I ask about his activity level. Is he walking in the yard? Is he doing his exercises? He gets one word out, "yes." Pauses to breathe.

His wife is off and running. Telling me about how many steps he is taking. When he naps, how long. Which exercises are hardest for him to do. I look at Amos. He looks at me. I look at her. She smiles. Her answer is again, exactly what I need to know clinically. *Healthcare.*

So it goes with every question I ask Amos.

I feel irritation shift towards frustration towards anger. My fists are clenched beneath the table. I'm sitting on the edge of my chair. It's becoming more challenging to keep my face and voice neutral. *Let him talk. Let him talk. Let him talk.* I want to roar but I don't. I want to stand up on my chair and scream. *It is not only about healthcare.*

Let him talk.

She's giving me all the answers, all the information I need to make clinical decisions. Write orders. Finish the visit efficiently. So much of her life is spent managing his medical ailments and medications. She's his nurse, caregiver, wife, manager, all in one. She never has a day off. She keeps him healthy and minimizes complications for so many chronic illnesses. She does it extremely well.

Yet here I am wanting to yell at her. I can't figure out how to tell her it's alright (and good) to *let him talk* without causing offense or dishonoring what she does for him. Let him answer these questions. In his own halting, messy, start-over-again-and-again way. Let him muddle through it. Let me muddle through it. It's what we do. *Soul care.*

I *know* you know all the information. I *know* you can communicate all of it more clearly and precisely but sometimes that isn't the point. Sometimes the point is to let the mess be the way it is. Embrace the slow, impractical, uncomfortable way of doing, of being. Because this is where the connection is. This is where the caring is. *Let him talk.*

I feel angry and incompetent. I'm embarrassed. I can't figure out how to navigate this situation. How can I respect her and the role she plays? While also respecting him and his right to speak in his own way?

I appreciate this woman so much for what she does. I know Amos wouldn't be as healthy as he is today without her. In truth, he would most likely not be alive. For that I am so very grateful for her. But also in truth, I hope she *doesn't* come to the next visit. Because even though it's efficient and smooth, I miss the mess and the struggle.

I miss letting him talk.

20

Independence.

Norma Jean (who goes by Faye) is a ninety-something year old woman. She scheduled to see me in the clinic where I work as a nurse practitioner. She shows up early. She tells the front desk when she checks in she is ready to rumble. The front desk messages me to let me know. *Oh boy. What are we going to rumble about?*

I refilled Faye's medications last week. She takes five prescription medications. Three of the five meds she takes once daily. The fourth med she takes twice daily. The fifth med she only takes half of a tablet three times a week. She prefers picking up three months of tablets at one time to save trips to the pharmacy. Makes sense to me. I ordered her three months of tablets with refills. I know I did this right.

I double check the math, the prescriptions. Everything is in order. *So what does she want to rumble about?*

I escort Faye into the exam room. She gets right to it. She is mad about the prescription for the half-tablet three times a week.

"Why did you rip me off?" Faye demands, as I close the exam room door. She sits down.

Whatever happened to hello? How are you? I'm concerned about...

"Did you think I wasn't paying attention? Only thirty tablets." She shakes the bottle at me. Rattle, rattle.

"All the rest have ninety or more!" She shakes one of those bottles at me for comparison. It certainly is louder. RATTLE, RATTLE.

I nod, preparing to speak but am denied the opportunity.

"Fix it," she states. "Fix it. Now."

Her level of anger seems out of proportion to the issue but I try to stay calm while ninety-plus years of anger squint at me from behind thick, smudged bifocals. She shakes the two pill bottles at me again. Rattle. Rattle. RATTLE. Rumble.

My mind errantly wanders to a song that finishes with boom-chicka-boom-rattle-rattle. I attempt to refocus.

I try to explain the math for the half tablets. How many tablets that adds up to over three months.

"If anything, I've overprescribed. You have more tablets than you need." I think I'm being helpful. I think I know what I'm doing. I know the math is correct. *Why is she so mad?*

Faye isn't moved. Her anger ratchets up. "I'm paying attention," Faye tells me in clipped, icy tones. "To everything. Fix. It." *Rattle. RATTLE. Shake. shake. Boom-chicka-boom.*

I attempt to explain safe practices in prescribing, why ninety tablets wouldn't be safe. I talk about risk of overdose if she were to mix up pills. This doesn't help. She stands up and tries to tower over me, all 4'11" of her. I remain seated. *Rattle-shake-boom-shake...*

"Fix it now," Faye repeats. Glowering ensues. *Shake shake shake. Rattle shake.* My calm is starting to slip.

Fix what? There is nothing to fix. know I did my part right. So what am I missing? Rattle-shake-boom-chicka-boom...

Finally, after ten minutes of trying to explain and out of complete exasperation (plus a little desperation) I say, "it sounds like you're really upset about this prescription."

I stop. I don't try to argue or explain. *Boom.*

She nods and sits down. The fight goes from a boil to a simmer. The air in the room calms. *Shake...*

"It sounds like you feel you were ripped off when you only got thirty tablets and not ninety or more like the others?" I wait again. *Rattle...*

Faye nods, even calmer. "Yes," she says. She does not yell at me. She sighs.

I wait again. *Chicka boom...*

She starts talking.

"My family thinks I can't take care of myself. They're looking for any reason to put me in... a... one of those places." Her hand waves dismissively in the air and she pinches her nose like something smells foul. She tells me she watches everything closely to make sure it's all orderly. No mistakes. She wants to stay in *her home.* She doesn't want to move.

She has funds to hire a caregiver if she needs one. She doesn't need one yet. She doesn't want her family to think she's missing medications or isn't on top of things. They'll move her, she fears. She's afraid the thirty tablets could be a reason. She desperately wants to stay in her home. *Boom. Rattle.*

I listen. I am humbled. *Boom chicka boom.*

She didn't come to the clinic needing me to explain the math of one-and-one-half tablets weekly. She needed me to listen.

I spent ten minutes explaining and teaching. Wasting her time and mine. Thinking I was giving her what she needed. But I had not bothered to see beyond her anger or her shaking pill bottles. *Until* I finally did. Until I stopped focusing on my agenda. Until I acknowledged what she was feeling, what she was telling me. I had to remain calm. I had to see her before I could help her. I also had to help her calm down. It's hard to have a discussion when you're angry.

Ultimately Faye said she understood thirty tablets was the right amount for the prescription. She was so concerned about making mistakes and having to move from her home she developed what she called "the tunnel vision." She couldn't think or see things clearly. *Rattle. RATTLE.*

We spent the remainder of the visit focusing on ways to keep her in her home. We talked about services she could start putting in place now to help maintain independence as long as possible. As I write this, nearly four years after that fateful visit, she's still living in *her home.*

It's so easy to get caught up in the importance of being right. It's so easy to lose your calm when someone is yelling at you and miss the bigger picture. Thirty pills is right. I forget that thirty pills may not be why this person is here. It may be something bigger or entirely different. It may require a little healthcare plus a little soul care. Stop and listen. Hear what the person in front of me is saying. Then we can get to work and make magic happen. Then as nurses, we can provide the kind of care that goes well beyond healthcare.

Rattle. Rattle. Boom. Chicka boom.

21

Gloves, please.

Luca arrived for his clinic appointment barely on time. Checked in. Then immediately went to the bathroom down the hall.

He was in the bathroom for well over thirty minutes. He completely missed his appointment as well as the next time slot after that. I saw two other patients who arrived early, in an attempt to stay on schedule. Staying on schedule is like serving an evil overlord who's whims change without warning. I often have little control over my schedule yet am held accountable for it anyway.

I was irritated when Luca returned from the bathroom, expecting to be seen immediately.

Luca is soft spoken and courteous. He generally says please and thank you. He insists I walk in front of him through a door. He waits to sit until I have sat. I see him regularly in clinic and these things never change.

Today he makes no comment about the length of time he was in the bathroom. He says nothing about the fact I am seeing him fifty minutes after his scheduled appointment.

I decide I'll talk with Luca about arriving in the clinic and being seen at your scheduled time. Our clinic is too busy to operate otherwise. Show up on time and be seen. That's it. *Deliver this message, clear and firm. Breathe in... Breathe out...*

For goodness sake. Do you know how late we are? Do you know every patient after you is going to be affected by this? It's not fair to them. Acknowledge it. Please.

My frustration is morphing into anger. Stomach twists. Jaw clenches. *Ugh. Do belly breathing... Stay calm.* This is not how I want to start a visit.

We enter the exam room and sit. I prepare to start but Luca speaks first.

"Gloves, please. Could you spare a pair of gloves for me?" Luca asks me.

My irritation ratchets up. I hold my breath. Anger seethes just under the surface.

Fifty minutes late and now you want gloves?? We are not a handing-out-gloves-for-free-clinic. In fact I recently had to go through training that explicitly told me I can't give supplies to patients. Giving supplies is stealing from the company. I'm not a thief. No gloves.

I look at Luca and waspishly explain, "unfortunately the clinic can't hand out gloves. Sorry."

But I'm not really sorry. I'm not my best self right now. Does he know that?

Luca nods and smiles. "Thank you anyways," he says. He bows his head a little. Shuffles his feet against the tiled floor.

Breathe in... Breathe out... Be calm.

I try to move on. On the surface he hasn't done anything terribly wrong. He's late. He asked for gloves. Yet it all hits me the wrong way today.

Luca seems oblivious to my irritation. He hums a little between the clinical questions I ask him as the visit progresses.

Calm down. Take deep breaths. Be professional. Breathe. Argh, stop that humming...

Luca answers my questions. He smiles. He hums. The clock ticks. *I hate that clock. I hate humming. I hate everything. This is not staying calm.*

"Tell me about your appetite," I say to Luca.

Deep breath. Refocus.

Luca shifts a little in the chair as he is telling me about what he eats each day. The smell hits me maybe ten seconds later. The smell is pungent and strong. Like an uncleaned urinal at a swimming pool. Like an outhouse that has been baking in the hot August sun. It's in that instant I fully understand why he's so late.

Why he asked me for gloves. *Gloves. Oh. Ohhh.*

The balloon of anger suddenly deflates inside. No more anger. In the empty space there is sadness. Futility.

I now try to understand why he didn't push me for the gloves, when I irritably explained I couldn't provide them. He certainly needs them.

With one olfactory whiff he gives me an entire lecture about dignity. The smell remains throughout the appointment. I manage the healthcare business as quickly as I can.

How can I make this right? How can I help him? He hasn't brought up the smell... Or the gloves again...

"Luca," I say, at the end of the visit, "do you need assistance getting cleaned up?" My eyes hold his as I ask.

"No," he says and looks down, not meeting my eyes for the first time. Not smiling. Not humming.

As Luca gets up and walks to the door I make a decision. I hand him a pair of gloves, two pairs actually.

The gloves represent more than healthcare. They represent shared humanity. They are the way I would hope someone would treat my dad if he was in the same situation. They are the way I would hope anyone would treat any other human in the same situation.

I curse my schedule, the clock, and the business of healthcare. To not have time to care for a man who needs help getting cleaned up. To be beholden to a schedule that is generally impossible to maintain. To work in a system that instructs me to not give away gloves. To feel guilty about giving gloves to a man who needs them.

A pair of gloves is a small price to pay to be able to show humanity still exists in the world of healthcare. There can be healthcare and there can be connection too. *Do better. Change lives for the better. Be a nurse.*

22

Devil or angel.

It's 1:59 in the morning. O'dark thirty. I'm driving well over the speed limit on the freeway to get to the hospital. I awoke from a deep sleep eight minutes earlier to the "beee-beee-beeeeeep" of my pager. I'm now wearing scrubs, beat up running shoes, and a light-weight jacket. I have thirty minutes, from the moment I'm paged, to be at the hospital. In the lab. Ready to receive a patient.

I work as a cath lab nurse. Tonight I'm part of a three-person-team. We were all paged in at 1:59 this morning. All three of us had worked the previous day. All three of us were most likely been sleeping when the pager summoned us. All three of us are scheduled to work this next day as well (in only five hours time).

But none of that is running through my mind. Instead I'm reciting the list of things I needed to do as soon as I get to the lab while my foot presses down on the gas pedal of my car. *Pull the pack. Turn on the defibrillator. Put on my lead. Pull meds. Syringes. Fluids. Tubing. Flushes.*

The "lab" is the cath lab or the cardiac catheterization lab. It's where you might go if you come into the Emergency Room (ER) with chest pain. The ER doctor, after running a few quick tests, diagnoses you with an acute MI (myocardial infarction) or heart attack. Our goal, at the time I worked in the cath lab, was to be in the lab, set up, and ready to go within thirty minutes of being paged. To have the offending coronary artery opened within ninety minutes of that patient arriving in the hospital. From the moment that pager goes off I'm on the clock. *Drive. Drive. Go. Go. Get there fast.*

I park and flash my badge to security. This is not my first time being paged in at night. Our team is called in often, especially this group of three. *We're lucky, I guess.*

I jog down the hall and up the stairs. I'm in the lab before 2:10 am. Just on my heels, our second team member arrives. We immediately get to work prepping the lab, pulling supplies.

It's amazing to me what I can do at two in the morning when I've done that particular something over and over again. The sterile table is prepped. I pull all the medications I think I might need. We turn on the c-arm, monitors and computers. Our third team member rolls in as the patient arrives with the doctor and group of ER nurses. It's 2:14 am. Twenty-three minutes earlier I was sound asleep in my bed. *I miss my warm bed.*

While we move the patient from the ER gurney to our table, the ER nurse gives me verbal report. We strap the patient to our table so he won't fall off the narrow surface onto the hard tile floor. We hook him up to our monitors, ECG, blood pressure, oxygen saturation, and defibrillator. The doctor and scrub tech are already scrubbing in at the sinks. The monitor tech is taking notes, recording everything that happens as it happens. The ER staff disappear back to the ER. We pop Garth Brooks into the CD player and get to work.

During report from the ER nurse I learned the patient has already been defibrillated once in the ambulance, when his heart went into a lethal arrhythmia. He hasn't needed another shock since arriving at the hospital. He was brought in from a party tonight after passing out. Luckily someone at the party was sober enough and clear-headed enough to call 911. The "sober-enough" person recognized this was not a "normal" passing out, if there is such a thing. Whoever that person was had probably saved this guy's life.

The guy, the patient, on our table was "drinking and drugging pretty hard" according to the medics. The number and names of drugs he sampled tonight is unknown right now. The patient is currently trying to sit up, stand up, or roll himself off the table despite being secured by large canvas and Velcro bands. He's covered in a blue sterile drape and the doctor is ready to access his femoral artery. And hopefully save his life. The guy needs to be still so we can do our jobs. Talking to him and reassuring him are not working to calm him down.

I approach him and try to explain (again) where he is.

"You're in the cath lab at the hospital. Please stop moving. We're trying to save your life sir."

He continues to thrash about.

"We think you're having a heart attack. We're getting ready to look at the arteries around your heart. It's possible one or more of them are blocked. You need to lay still."

He responds by trying to kick the sterile drape off his legs. And he growls.

"You're strapped to the table because it's unsafe for you to move while we do this procedure. We need you to be still. We're trying to save your life."

He whips his head back and forth and attempts to sit up while growling more loudly.

After my last attempt to verbally reach him, he finally focuses his wild, dilated, bloodshot eyes on me. He stops growling and starts screaming. *Not an improvement.*

"Devil.... You've come for me. Devil! The devil is cometh. Devil woman. Devil woman. Aaaaaayyyyye. Devil!"

The doc, the scrub tech, the monitor tech all pause and look at me in my blue scrubs and running shoes. I'm also wearing a lead vest and skirt (similar to a lead apron but two pieces instead of one) that are covered in a printed red and yellow flame pattern. I love this lead! I never have to hunt for it. Everyone else has some version of blue, black, or navy and they all look the same hanging on the racks. My lead is easy to find, covered in flames.

"Devil," the patient continues to scream on repeat, becoming more agitated. The doc can't start the case until the patient calms down. The patient needs to be still. Time is important here.

The doc looks at me, "well that's a new one," he drily comments.

He follows this up with a request for sedation so we can get to work.

I comply. Sedation is delivered to the patient. The patient calms down. The case begins.

In less than ten minutes the doc finds and visualizes the blocked artery. An image is saved to one screen so he knows exactly where he is working. I drop the supplies he requests on the sterile table for the scrub tech to prep. The coronary artery is quickly opened and stented.

Our team does this a lot. It's a good feeling to be fast and efficient at something like this. Sometimes we even get to go back home and sleep a bit more before the day shift starts. *Maybe I'll get more sleep tonight...*

But that is not tonight.

Because sometimes, when a coronary artery is reopened, and the heart suddenly regains blood flow (where it's been lost), the heart muscle becomes a bit "angry." The heart rhythm might go into an unhealthy rhythm, too fast or too slow. A patient might suddenly feel more chest pain. Blood is suddenly flowing where it wasn't. As a cath lab nurse I have to be prepared for this. The patient might need medications or to be defibrillated. I watch the cardiac rhythm on the monitor. *Waiting and hoping everything remains normal. It doesn't.*

This guy promptly goes into v-tach (ventricular tachycardia, a generally lethal arrhythmia, unless treated). We already have defibrillator pads on him. I start charging the defibrillator. The quickest way to fix v-tach is to deliver a shock of electricity to the heart to reset the electrical system. Just as I'm about to shock his heart back into a regular rhythm, the patient opens his eyes and looks at me. He is perfectly still.

"Angel," he whispers, despite me still wearing my flame-covered lead. Despite the high-pitched whine of the defibrillator charging. Despite the fact I've done nothing to deserve being called an angel at this moment.

Then he projectile vomits all over me, the closest monitor, the floor and everything else within a six foot radius. Red, brown, pink, green, small yellow chunks. They hang and drip on my lead, the equipment, the floor.

I call for "all clear." I deliver the shock. I try not to breathe through my nose.

With that one shock of electricity his cardiac rhythm stabilizes. I push medications into the IV as ordered by the doc to keep him stable and follow them up with saline flushes. Then the doc tells me to go get changed. I don't need to be asked twice. *Yuck.*

Another life saved.

After I quickly wipe off and change our team delivers the guy to the ICU for further care. The ICU nurse tells me I stink, despite having fresh scrubs on. I warn her to watch out if the patient calls her "angel." My team laughs.

I'm grateful for my team. This work would be impossible otherwise. Having a team that supports you and has your back is soul care for nurses. Having a team that high-fives you after saving a life, despite you being covered in barf, is priceless.

After a more thorough wipe-down in the staff bathroom at the hospital it's 5:45am. Not enough time to go home. *Sigh*. But definitely enough time to grab a quick nap on a couple lunch room chairs shoved together to make a bench. The three of us take over different corners and nap under hospital blankets (fresh from the blanket warmer). Our next shift starts at 7:00 am.

Don't let anyone tell you medicine is glamorous. It's not. The days can be really long. The hours grueling. The work soul-sucking on the worst of days. But it can also be rewarding, to save a life. To be there when a new life enters the world. To be present when an old life leaves. You can be part of a really great team. And you might get a nickname that lasts like "devil woman" or "angel."

23

No hospice.

Bonita did not want hospice. She wanted to live. There isn't much more to say than that. But I'll tell her story anyway. She had cancer. It isn't part of her plan, but cancer never is. Bonita was young enough to still be working full time with retirement in her somewhat distant future. Her daughter was pregnant with her first grandchild. Her son was recently out of college. Bonita was planning on living a long time. She did not want hospice.

She wanted a grandchild and lots of years of life. But the cancer was metastatic (meaning it had spread to other places in her body). She had gone through all the treatments and surgeries, then a few more. She weighed eighty pounds when I met her. She only wanted chemotherapy and cures. But her body had other ideas.

Hospice was ordered by her doctor, despite her not wanting it.

I speak with her husband on the phone before I arrive. He says he should meet me in the driveway. "Do not come up to the house. Do. Not." He needs to talk with me first.

This isn't unusual. Many people like to meet outside before they let me into their homes. If I was inviting someone into my home to care for my dying loved one, I'd probably want to assess them first as well. Outside in the driveway, in daylight.

So, I meet Earl in front of their house.

What I'm not prepared for is the reason for Earl's absolute certainty I cannot ever, NEVER, tell Bonita, his wife, I work with hospice.

"Because she'll raise heaven and hell, then die on the spot. Then she'll haunt me forever. For-*ever*," he emphasizes the last word, saying it twice.

I cannot tell her I work for hospice. So that's a problem.

I explain to Earl I can be introduced as a visiting nurse. But I won't lie if Bonita asks me about hospice, death, or dying. I'll tell her the truth.

"You can't tell her," he says again. We're at an impasse.

We stand in the driveway, warm sun on our backs. Birds chirp. Cars whoosh past. I can smell sweet, cut grass somewhere nearby. I wait.

Earl shuffles his feet. Small pebbles scatter and roll down the driveway. I watch them roll, find purchase, and stop.

"Why can't I tell her?" I ask.

"Because she doesn't want this. She doesn't want to die." More shuffling of feet. More pebbles rolling.

"Okay, that's fair. Most people don't want to die. But with hospice you don't just die right away. That's not how hospice works...."

I trail off and wait again. It's generally not my way to be forceful. If they choose to not have hospice services that's fine. I'll update the doctor who ordered the services. We'll move on with our lives.

Earl shuffles his feet again as we stand in the sun. More pebbles go plinking down the driveway. "I know, I know" he mutters to himself. "I know what you are saying. But she will die. She'll just die, on the spot, she will. Then she'll haunt me."

"She doesn't have to be in hospice," I gently tell Earl. "This isn't a required service. A doctor ordered it, but you have every right to say no. It's easy to update the doc. I can leave. It's fine."

I prepare to go but he lays a hand on my arm.

"Wait," he says.

We stand there in the sun. A lawnmower roars to life. I hear a car door slam followed by the beep of an alarm being activated. I wait. It's his decision and hers.

He makes up his mind. Feet still shuffling but there are no pebbles left to disperse.

"Go in," he says. "But I'm not going with you. I'll be back in sixty minutes." He looks at his watch.

"Do your thing... and if she's alive when I return, well, good." He nods.

"If not... well... if I'm not here then perhaps she won't haunt me."

I nod, feeling unsure about this haunting thing. *Will she haunt me, if I'm here when she dies?*

Earl nods at the front door. "It's unlocked. Go up the stairs, second door on the right. She's expecting a visiting nurse. Good luck." Then he's gone.

I'm left standing in the driveway. I walk up the stone path and knock lightly on the large dark wooden door. No answer.

The door is unlocked, as Earl said it would be. I enter a lived in, loved in, slightly outdated but comfortable sort of home with stained oak wood floors and faded oriental rugs. Sheer drapes hang on the windows. Plants are everywhere. Books overflow all the available surfaces. There's a smell like Italian meat sauce drifting down a hallway. Mail lies in an untidy heap on an entryway table along with gloves, a purse, an apple, a vase of dead flowers, and a box of dry pasta.

The staircase is straight ahead and I call "hello" as I climb the worn oaken steps. They creak with the slightest of protest but otherwise the house is peaceful, quiet. At the top of the stairs I turn and find the door, second on the right.

I knock lightly. Bonita answers immediately. "Come in." Sharp and crisp.

I enter the room, immediately engulfed, swallowed, overwhelmed by light and color. Light coming in from windows and skylights, bright and welcoming and shocking too. Color as if the room itself is a rainbow and each section is dedicated to a color. *Where is Bonita?*

Her voice helps me find her. "I am here," she says crisply, apparently aware I need help locating her. All business. "You are the nurse. The hospice nurse. The one I do not want. But here you are. You. Are. The. Hospice. Nurse." Her voice reminds me of a recorded voice, slightly mechanical and clipped.

She pauses and looks at me from her bed. The bed is giant and yellow, covered with layers of white fluff and pillows. She is lying in the middle, propped up on many pillows. It reminds me of a very small bird, in an overly large nest.

"Yes," I say, "I am the nurse. And yes, I am with hospice." *Well, that didn't take long...Are you going to die now? Will you haunt me?*

She looks at me again. She does not die on the spot.

Large sunken eyes in a too large head on a too small frame. Skin stretched taut in places, drooping and sagging in others. No hair. She blinks.

"Okay," she says. She nods. "I can work with you." The voice is crisp and commanding, a force all its own. But the body is so very frail.

"Sooooo hospice nurse..." A pause. "Here's what you need to know. I do not want hospice. I do not want you here. I will not die here. I will not die with hospice. I will die fighting. I will not die in my beautiful house with my beautiful room and my beautiful things. I will not die with hospice. Do you understand that?"

"Yes" I nod, feeling very much like I'm a student and she is the teacher. The ground feels slippery underneath me.

This is not how hospice is supposed to go, not how hospice usually goes... How do I provide hospice care to someone who doesn't want it? Do I even stay, since she clearly doesn't want me here?

I start to explain, I don't have to be here. If she doesn't want hospice I can leave. She interrupts me.

"Good. Good." The giant head wobbles forward and back on the twig that is her neck balanced on her shoulders. The eyes bore into me, dark and assessing.

She continues, "I will not die on the spot either. Though that is what I told my husband would happen if he allowed hospice to come in. But I am sure he told you that. Did he not?" She looks at me expectantly.

"Yes, he mentioned it before he left." *A few times...*

"Good." The head bobs again. "And I see you came anyway, despite his warnings of instant death and hauntings. Good."

Are you sure that's good? I'm re-evaluating right now...

She wheezes, laughs, then starts coughing. I notice the white comforters shift up and down as she coughs. It looks like she is floating above the bed, holding court, and coughing.

"You tell me the truth," she says, after the coughing stops. It is a statement, not a question. She pauses and waits.

I realize I'm supposed to answer this. "Yes," I respond cautiously. Not sure what else there is to say. "I'll tell you the truth... I'll try."

I'm grateful I had the conversation with Earl outside. I'm grateful she knew immediately. Now it's my turn to pause and wait. This dance we're doing, I don't know these steps but I'm willing to learn.

How do I provide hospice for someone who doesn't want it? Let's figure this out together.

"Good. So, I will repeat my truth again and you will listen again. I will *not* die with hospice. I will *not* die here. I *will* die fighting. I *will* see you in my home because you, hospice nurse, will help me do these things. You will help me live." The voice so clear, the eyes so large, the colors of the room so bright. It feels like I'm in another world. Briefly I wonder, is she a witch?

Then she laughs again and tells me one more truth. "I *will* come back and haunt my husband." More cackling. *She might be a witch...*

That was the day I met Bonita when she started hospice. Hospice, which she did not want, but accepted into her home, because she wanted to live. She never called me anything other than "hospice nurse" during the time I came to visit her.

Bonita was in hospice for about four months during which time she gained enough weight and recovered enough to be able to resume chemotherapy for her cancer. During that time I saw her twice a week. My job was to help her manage symptoms like pain and nausea while she did her best to gain weight and strength. I listened to what she wanted. I tried to support her. I provided the healthcare she needed, knowing she could still die in her home, despite not wanting to. Earl and I never crossed paths again.

Bonita resumed chemotherapy and stopped hospice as soon as she could. She didn't want both. Sometimes people undergo palliative chemotherapy (chemo that isn't curative) and have hospice as well. This wasn't for Bonita, as she told me at the very beginning. She knew what she wanted. This did not deviate.

Bonita did not die at home. She did not die with hospice.

She did get to meet her first grandchild.

Then, weeks later, Bonita died during a chemotherapy infusion. She died fighting.

I don't know if she came back to haunt Earl, but I've always wondered.

Bonita was incredibly ill and very easily could have died while on our hospice service. However she had plans. She accepted our services because she knew (hoped) we could get her pain, nausea, and poor appetite better controlled than they were. Once that happened she was able to eat more and gain some weight.

Bonita was not a typical hospice patient but I still think it's important to share her story. She reminds me to keep an open mind and to think outside the box. Working with her was like learning a new dance with a new partner. I had to be open to what she was asking for and also work within the framework of what I could do or provide. Bonita reminds me to think differently about obstacles, perhaps the way to get past the obstacle is not around or under, but instead to walk straight into it and come out the other side. She did not want hospice but hospice most likely helped her live her life longer than she would have otherwise.

24

Coins.

Sami is a quiet man who moved to the United States with his wife and two small sons. He brought a few random heirlooms, hopes for a better life, and a coin collection. The collection was handed down from his grandfather to his father to him.

Each coin is sealed in a plastic box with a clear lid. The coins each sit on a small piece of foam. The box is pain-stakingly labeled in small dark print. The name of the coin. Where the coin came from. Its worth at the time. Sami added to the collection throughout his life. He wanted his sons to have it, part old-world, part new. His wife shows me the drawers where the coins are neatly stored in rows. She tells me this collection is his most prized possession.

When I first meet Sami he shares stories with me about each coin, where the coin came from, and who in his family collected it. The coins are from all over the world due to his extensive travels. He can still remember how each coin came to be in the collection. Despite Sami's memory rapidly failing memory, he still remembers his coins.

After a few months working with Sami I notice he can't always tell me his name or where he lives. He can't remember the month or the year. But he can tell me stories about the engravings and images on each small piece of metal. A bird. A building. A person. He loves his coins and the memories they represent. They're a connection to where he came from, his heritage and history. They're meant to be a gift for his family. His face comes alive as he describes each coin and the attached memories. Eyes bright, mouth smiling. *I can see you Sami as you talk about your coins. I see who you are despite this disease that is taking you away.*

But Sami's memory gets worse, as it does with advancing dementia. As a hospice nurse, I missed Sami's early years of dementia. I'm only there for the last ten months. The decline in those last ten months is rapid and terminal.

About six months after I meet him, there are days when Sami doesn't remember the coins. During my visits we often sit in his study. I listen to his lungs. I ask his wife about what Sami is eating and drinking. We discuss sleep patterns. Sami sits there and looks at his coins. But he rarely speaks. One or two words at the most.

He runs his fingers over coin boxes and studies the writing, as if it's something foreign or new to him. I suppose as his brain changes the coins and the writing do become foreign. He holds the boxes, testing their weight, caressing their covers, then putting them away. His expression blank.

Where did you go, Sami? These are your coins. This is your collection. I wish you could remember them...

Sami eats less. Sleeps during the day. Is awake all night. He loses weight. He loses more of his memories and himself. Many days the change is slow, almost imperceptible. Then suddenly one day a large chunk of memory will be missing, like an iceberg breaking off into the sea, floating away. What that chunk represents is unclear until suddenly Sami doesn't recognize his son or his cat or know how to swallow food. Unpredictable and heart breaking yet inevitable with this disease called dementia.

I know you're in there Sami. We're still here too. Caring for you.

Then there's the one day I come to visit. The day when his wife opens the door and she's crying, sobbing, inconsolable. Speaking in their first language, over and over, the same words. All I can decipher is pain, sadness, loss.

Oh my gosh, did he die? Is he gone? Has he hurt himself? What happened?

Expecting the worst I enter the house to find Sami alive. He is wearing a robe, sitting in a chair near his desk in "the coin room." He's wearing pajama pants and one slipper. There's a small smear on his left cheek that must be remnants of breakfast. A faint smell of vinegar hangs in the air.

And surrounding him on the floor and desk are coins. *Coins. Coins. Coins.*

Oh no. Oh no oh no oh no oh no.

Hundreds of open boxes are haphazardly scattered amongst the shining, glittering coins. Labels with small, dark writing tossed about like leaves in the autumn wind. Sami hums to himself, blissfully unaware of the damage that's been done. None of it ever to be put right again. *Lost. Lost. Lost. It's all lost.*

Pain. Sadness. Loss. His wife is still saying the same words over and over. I understand. Without speaking their language I know now what she's saying.

It's lost. *It's lost. It's all lost.* These words speak of sadness and loss. The repeated loss that happens with dementia over weeks, months, years.

The loss of these coins and what they stand for. The loss of Sami. It's dreadful. My gut twists as I take Sami's hands and look into his eyes. These aren't my coins but I so desperately want to fix it, to offer something other than, "this is what happens with dementia." I want to offer something other than healthcare and platitudes.

I want to place each coin back in its box with its small piece of foam padding. To apply each carefully written label. To tuck all the boxes back into the drawers where they belong. Ready to be handed down to his family. I want to turn back time.

It's all lost. Lost. Lost.

Instead I hold Sami's withered hands. I gently help him up to standing. He shuffles behind me without protest.

"Pretty," he says, as we leave the room of glittering mess. I nod.

"Yes, Sami, they are pretty," I say.

Tears burn at the edges of my eyes as we walk out of this room of sparkling coins. He pats my hand. He hums a little.

"Dance?" he says to me questioningly. I'm surprised by the word.

Does he remember how to dance? How can he remember dancing? Yet not remember his coins? Lost. Lost. Lost.

Over time I learn there's no stopping the loss with dementia. At least there wasn't twenty years ago when this happened. There is no control. Yet even with the loss there may still be love and dignity. For anyone who has lost someone to dementia or is caring for someone with dementia, my heart goes out to you. I am sending you love and light, for the way is often long and lonely. You are not alone.

While all chronic diseases result in decline and disability, I find dementia to be especially hard on the caregivers. Hard on the soul. The scars I carry from loving people with dementia run deep. The privilege of caring for someone in their final days, weeks, months of this disease is the balm. Caring for someone at the end of life as dementia takes them, that is pure soul care.

25

Groceries.

Impending loss leads to different responses. Freeze, don't move. Forget to breathe. Run, run, run away. Hide in a dark cave. Attack. I've found the response to impending loss is unpredictable at best.

I think about this, as I approach the front door of an apartment at 2:32 in the morning. I'm the on-call hospice nurse for our service tonight. I was paged at 1:49am. The night is dark with only a few bright stars. There are sprinklers next door, spraying lightly over the grass. I smell the water and coolness in the air. I shiver in my light-weight sweatshirt. I prepare to ring the bell next to the yellow front door of A6.

Margaret's partner, Joan, opens the door before my finger presses the bell. Joan's eyes don't blink, but instead stare blankly past my shoulder. She doesn't smile. She leads me to the living room. No words are spoken. She's in her cave it would seem. She's hiding. Death is near. I've seen this before.

A hospital bed sits in the center of the living room. It's the only place it fits in their small, cramped apartment. Margaret lies in the bed. Her breathing is shallow, irregular, like gasping but deeper. And harder to listen to for those on the living side. Agonizing, agonal. Margaret is actively dying.

Joan knows what's happening. She's been through this before, with a different partner twenty years ago. Joan stares into the dark night out the window. Not blinking. She's here but not fully here. I quietly ask Joan questions.

"How long has Margaret been like this?"

Joan nods as a response.

"What medications have you given already?"

Joan points to a paper on the living room table with names of medications and numbers scrawled down. A pencil missing its eraser sits nearby. Joan gave Margaret a small dose of morphine one hour ago.

"Where are the medications in case we need more?"

Joan points to the kitchen. She still speaks no words. I let her know she can ask me any questions if she has them.

I settle into my work. Finding comfort in the familiarity of listening to the heart and lungs. Feeling for pulses where they no longer pulse. Margaret's hands and feet are cold. Only the deep central pulses are still palpable, just barely.

I talk quietly to Margaret as I do my work. Never certain how much a person is here and how much they're elsewhere. I've done all of this before in different rooms, with different people. And despite having it done it before it is always different and feels new with each person. The work is slow and methodical. Joan stands across the room, staring out the window. Still not speaking.

As I pull a blanket back up over Margaret's body, Joan announces she needs groceries. The words break the silence. I wince.

"Canned beans. Apples. Soy milk. Garlic. Possibly cinnamon," she says with no emotion. Still looking out the dark window. Not looking at Margaret.

Panic swirls around Joan as she grabs her coat, purse, shoes. Anxiety spurs her onward to the door, the darkness, the escape. She allows herself one glance back to the bed, to me, to Margaret. Her partner of many years lies there breathing short, shallow breaths. One glance back to the imminent unfolding of life ending tonight.

Then Joan is gone.

I'm briefly frustrated. To be here at 2:57 in the morning. Instead of in my warm bed, asleep, and dreaming. But this is the work I have signed up to do, the service I am privileged to provide.

Joan is gone. She's relinquished Margaret and I to the ticking of the clock, the whirr of the refrigerator in the next room, the fizz of sprinklers still running next door. She's relinquished us to the march of time.

Joan has escaped to fluorescent lights, aisles of cans, the task of foraging for food where it is plentiful. Canned beans. Apples. Soy milk. Garlic. Possibly cinnamon.

I refocus and return to my work. I let Margaret know in a whisper, Joan has run out briefly for groceries, repeating her list of foods.

Placing pillows here, tucking blankets there, I carefully position Margaret in the bed. Margaret's breathing is quieter now. Not gasping. Not gurgling. A quiet whisper nearly lost beneath the noise of the ticking clock.

I study the brightly colored afghans decorating every soft surface. I wonder, *who made them?* The bright yarn. The squares, triangles, and hexagons. These afghans tell a story of love, brightness, warmth. I wish I could ask someone about their history and meaning.

But I'm alone. Joan is at the store. Margaret is gone now, dead.

Within minutes of me telling her Joan left for groceries, she left too. I felt it, ever so subtle. A few shallow breaths, then no more. A change in the energy of the room. So I sit. Admire the afghans. Wait for Joan to return. Hum "Amazing Grace" quietly to myself.

People used to tell me the dying may pick their time. They may choose when to die and who to have with them. They may choose to protect someone by waiting until that person is gone. I didn't believe it until I experienced it. There are many things like this in nursing, things I didn't believe until I saw them or experienced them.

I believe now. I've seen it happen. Joan knew she couldn't be here when it happened. She escaped to canned beans. Apples. Soy milk. Garlic. Possibly cinnamon. Margaret waited, she picked her time, knowing Joan was gone.

Not much later, Joan returns to the small apartment leaving two bags of groceries at the door. She takes off her shoes but leaves on her coat. She walks over to the bed where Margaret lies, still, warm. I've been holding Margaret's hand, afraid to break contact completely.

As Joan climbs into the bed to hold her I let go of Margaret's hand. Joan lies next to Margaret's body with silent tears falling, wearing her now heavy coat of grief.

26

Grief & gratitude.

"I'm going to be here six more months," Grant tells me. This is how he starts our visit in the clinic where I work as a nurse practitioner.

"Oh. You're moving?" I reply, surprised. He has lived here for many decades. I didn't know he was thinking of moving.

"No, I'm dying," Grant says. "Twelve months, maybe." He nods his head, up and down.

"Oh." Deep breath and pause. I shake my head back and forth in response to his affirmative nodding.

"I see," I say, grateful my voice sounds steady.

Yet I don't see. Why six months? Why twelve months? Who told you this?

Luckily Grant fills the silence that remains after "I see."

"I just saw Cardiology. They can't do much more... They said maybe six to twelve months... If I'm lucky. It's okay." He smiles at me and continues.

"I knew this was coming. They told me I had six to twelve months over ten years ago. But this time I know they're right. I'm tired." He slumps in his chair.

Yes, I know. So tired. I see it. But...
I nod again. "I see. But..."
Sigh. I don't want you to die.

And yet, I *do* see. I've been seeing for the past two years. The slow decline. The increased hospitalizations. The titration of medications. The knowledge there aren't any new medications that can be tried or titrated. Every month I see him, when he's not in the hospital. Every month for nearly two years.

I check his blood. We take care of healthcare trying to maintain what health he has. Then we chat.

We talk of airplanes, baked bread, and the crossword. We lament the Friday crossword and how many words we leave empty, both being lovers of the puzzles. We do the work he comes to do. But we also visit about the traffic, the never-ending construction, and the local football team.

He tells me about his wife and her flowers. She's trying a new variety of zinnias this summer. We chat about when to plant tomatoes, who has the best fish in town, and where to buy cherries. Instead of immediately ending the visit when the work is done I spend a few minutes chatting about life, tending to soul care. It's the part I love the most.

I look forward to my monthly visits with Grant. I'm able to navigate the business of healthcare that needs to be completed but also enjoy the time I have with this man. Chatting and enjoying his company.

Now, today, I find out I may only have six more months with him. Six more visits. That feels both unacceptable but inevitable. Knowing what I know about cardiac physiology and seeing what I see each month I think we'll be lucky indeed if we get six more visits. So today I'll count myself very lucky, because today we got one more.

You see, we all die. It's a tricky fact of life, often ignored or pushed aside, in Western culture. Yet it remains incontrovertible. We all die.

Sometimes I think Western culture has done us a great disservice by ignoring the finiteness of life. Because within those boundedness of beginnings and endings is where life becomes most precious and fragile. This is where so much deep, powerful living occurs, in the moments when we realize this life (our life) does not stretch on into the forever. It ends.

So next, I will start to wrestle with that combination of grief and gratitude that are so hard to reconcile when they exist together in the same room at the same moment in time. Someone should make a word for that combination and put it in the Friday crossword.

"Griefitude."

I shared this story with a friend before publishing it. She wisely said the word for the Friday crossword puzzle should be 'griefitude.'

A mixture of gratitude for what you have and grief for what you are losing or have lost. I could not have summed it up any better.

27

Valentine's cards.

Shonda has cancer. The kind that spreads. The kind that can't be treated any longer. She tried all the treatments and the experiments. She underwent chemo, surgery, and radiation. She took trips to Mexico and South America. She fasted and juiced. She ate nothing but cabbage. She tried energy treatments, crystals, every healer she could find. But the cancer spread more. And more.

Shonda is married to her high-school sweetheart. They have three kids, all still young. Her kids go to the same elementary she went to, when she was growing up. She volunteers at the school every week. She works part-time as a Labor & Delivery nurse. She runs 5ks for charity and plays with her kids in the yard. That is, she did, until the cancer.

She has a white house with black shutters and a big, leafy tree in front. There's a rope swing in the tree. The backyard is filled with balls, a trampoline, and soft green grass to run around on. She has a tan fluffy dog who's always underfoot and loves to flop on your lap if you sit down. But she also has the cancer.

Shonda can't eat or drink much because it all comes back up. Nothing stays down because of where the cancer is and where it's spreading. She's getting IV (intravenous) nutrition and fluids, which isn't very common in hospice. But our hospice agreed to do it for a couple weeks. It gives her time.

Shonda needs time.

As her hospice nurse, having only known her for three weeks, I can already see time is running out.I know the world will be less bright when she is gone.

Emotional boundaries in hospice are important. Both for the patient but also for the nurse too. Hospice nurses are not supposed to become emotionally attached to their patients, but I am with Shonda. Shonda's my patient, but she's also become my friend. And my friend's time is running out.

In our weekly hospice meeting all the staff discuss Shonda's case. The IV nutrition and fluids are divisive. Some people agree we should do it to for a few weeks to buy her time. Others says we're breaking the rules. I try to explain why it's important and why we should keep providing fluids and nutrition.

But it comes out all wrong. It comes out full of anger and sadness and emotion. I'm too close to this case, this person.

I yell and glare at my colleagues. "Shonda is trying to find Valentine's Day cards. To write messages for her kids and her husband. She knows she'll be dead by mid-February. It's her favorite holiday. Valentine's Day. And she'll be dead."

So there! I think crossly. *She's trying to find Valentine's Day cards and it's October. October!*

I'm edgy, twitchy. My heart pounds. My head hurts.

Dead. Dead. Dead. Shonda will be dead.

I start crying as I finish yelling. Crying is what I do when I get angry and overwhelmed. I stop. I stand up and walk out. Because I have nothing left to yell. Because I am embarrassed. *I am in the wrong here. I am not supposed to care this much. I am not supposed to yell.*

The team lets me go. They give me space.

Ironically, the same day I yell at my colleagues (and lose control), is the same day Shonda finds Valentine's cards. She handwrites messages to her husband and her kids, seals each card, and places the envelopes on her bedside table.

The next day, she dies.

I'm at her house for a routine nurse visit. While I am putting away my stethoscope, after just listening to her beating heart and breathing lungs, she dies. I'm not expecting her to die.

It's really fast and really sudden. It's not pretty or peaceful. I'm there, yet there is absolutely nothing I can do to make it anything other than what it is. Her husband recognizes what's happening before I do and calls the kids to come. For the last moments.

After she dies, I cry in the bathroom. Silently, because I'm embarrassed. And so very sad. I don't want her family to see me cry. Me, the nurse, who's supposed to know what to do and help shepherd them through this process. I cry while we're waiting for the mortuary to arrive. While her husband and kids sit with her body. While her mom and dad sit in the living room. While her brother sits outside in the grass in the backyard. While the dog flops across her unmoving feet, recognizing something is changed and cannot be unchanged.

I cry and know I've crossed a boundary line.

I'm not supposed to be this sad. This attached. What do I do?

Boundaries can be tricky. There isn't always a clear line. In retrospect, the moment I realized I was too close, too attached, is the moment I should have asked my manager to reassign the case. But this had never happened to me before. I didn't recognize it at the time. I know better now.

When I studied physics I learned about the space where water and air coexist. A space of airy water or watery air, not clearly one or the other, the particles are mixed. That's me, standing in Shonda's bathroom. Crying. Not quite water. Not quite air. A mix of both. Caring as a nurse and losing a friend at the same time.

Boundaries exist for a reason though, for the patient's safety and also for the nurse. It's alright to care deeply, but I also have to remember to take care of myself too. Over the years of working in nursing I've become much better about recognizing and protecting healthy boundaries. I've also become more comfortable asking for help and saying "I'm too close." This is something that has required experience, time and growth.

Shonda stays with me in my heart. Years later, I still remember those cards, the three, vivid pink envelopes with her handwriting. Sitting on the bedside table in October. On the day she died. Waiting to be given to her loved ones (in five more months) on Valentine's Day.

***

The stories I've included in this section titled "Growing," span all throughout my nursing career. Because if there's one thing I want you to know, it's that you're constantly growing as a nurse. (Even if you've been a nurse for a long time.) Many of these stories are moments when I was deeply uncomfortable. Growth often is uncomfortable when you're in it.

There's asking questions I don't want to ask but know I need to ask. There's hope. There's navigating healthcare systems and providing care for patients, when the two things don't work well together. There's death and messy endings. There are boundaries broken and pain. There are decisions about what kind of team to be a part of and when to leave. There's the realization that healthcare is not glamorous but it can still be amazingly rewarding.

Twenty years into my nursing career I consistently find more opportunities to grow. This section of the book on "Growing," could be the largest. But I also think in some ways it is the most painful to write and reflect upon. Some of these moment are not my proudest ones. I hope by sharing them, you may avoid some of the mistakes I made or may be better prepared when faced with a challenging situation. Either way, please know that constant growth and change are simply part of being a nurse, whether you're brand new or have been practicing for decades.

Blooming

" Do the best you can until you know better,
then when you know better,
do better. "

- Maya Angelou

28

Wilt (Part 2).

I frequently see a pleasant seventy-year-old man in the clinic. We do the work of healthcare but we also chat about life in between. That's my favorite part, the chatting.

My garden is discussed a lot. It's a safe topic. Today my patient is more excited than usual to discuss gardening. He wants to get into gardening before we've even started the business of healthcare. His seventy-year-old frame bounces on the exam table. His pale, bony feet kick back and forth.

What is he so excited about?

"I went to get my groceries this weekend," he tells me, eyes bright. He bounces again on the exam table.

"When I got there I got my cart and started my shopping. At the front of the store, I noticed one sad, dead-looking tomato plant. I decided, if it's still there after I do my shopping I'd buy it."

I nod as I listen to his heart and lungs. I check his blood pressure while he is seated and standing.

He continues. "I circled back around and there it was! Droopy and dry but waiting for me." He smiles a big gummy smile. He's not put in his dentures today.

Must remember to ask him if his dentures are giving him trouble? Is he eating okay?

He starts talking again before I can ask.

"I looked at the sad little thing and thought to myself, you need a home. I've got a lovely little spot in my front yard with dark brown earth and lots of afternoon sun. I decided right then to bring him home. Did I do good?" he asks me.

The question catches me off guard.

Did I do good?

I nod in affirmation. *Yes. Yes.* "Yes, you did great," I say and smile.

He carries on. "We often chat about your tomatoes at our visits. They need good earth. Sun. Water."

He ticks each one off on his gnarled fingers.

"I can easily water this spot. It's just next to my door an' I can pop out easily to give Wilt some company. We can chat. And watch life as it passes by the front stoop."

"Wilt?" I ask while feeling for pulses in his wrists.

"Yes, Wilt!" he replies with another gummy smile.

"I named him. I have conversations with him. I told him I was coming to see you today." His feet bounce back and forth. It's the most alive this man has ever looked to me in the many years I've been seeing him in clinic.

"Wilt," I say and smile back at him, nodding my head as I move on to check for swelling in his ankles.

He named his tomato plant Wilt. My heart swells.

"I think a lot, 'bout how many people take care of me," he says.

"So many people, helping me stay strong and alive. I think about Wilt an' it just seemed the thing to do. So many people tending to me. I want something to tend too."

This brings me pause. I stop the work I'm doing. I sit. I smile. Look him in the eye.

"You did wonderful," I say. I feel my eyes tear up a bit, my heart swell a bit more. I ask him if I can give him a hug.

He nods yes. We hug.

I float through the rest of the day. Happy. Content.

All because of a man fighting to live another day and a tomato plant named Wilt.

These are the golden moments that keep me coming back to healthcare and nursing practice. Your moments may be something different, prepping someone for surgery, running a code, helping someone discharge back to home. For me, it's the unexpected moments of human connection. It's the stories and small things that make me realize we are more alike than we think. We are all unique but there is an undercurrent of small, human moments that connects us more than we often realize. I continue to be honored to hear the stories and connect with so many beautiful souls in this world.

29

Soul mates.

Melissa and Kate had been friends since they were teenagers, meeting sometime in the middle of an awkward seventh grade year. They grew up together. Traveled together. Started careers together. For a long time they were roommates. Then Kate met "the one," got married, and moved outside the city. Melissa didn't meet "the one." She stayed in the city, busy launching her dream career.

I meet Melissa and Kate on the first day I come to visit for hospice. They tell me stories of their time spent in different countries and adventures they had growing up. They tell me about Kate's kids. They tell me about Melissa's business and career. They do not tell me about the cancer.

Melissa has "the ultimate career," in her words. There's glamour, money, fame and fun. She travels the world. People know who she is. She can walk into restaurants without reservations. She can cut lines. Her picture might show up in a newspaper or magazine occasionally. She loves all of this. She eventually sets up her own "shop," her own business the way she wants it to be. She starts teaching what she's learned to the next generation.

Despite Melissa focusing on her career and Kate leaving the industry, having kids, and moving outside of town, they stay close. They're best friends.

"Soul mates," they say when I ask them about their long-lasting friendship. "It's simple as that. Soul. Mates." Then they smile at each other and hug.

Melissa was diagnosed with cancer the day after her fiftieth birthday. She has no family, no kids. Her only close friend, who isn't part of her "career world" is Kate. She turns to Kate immediately when she gets the diagnosis. The cancer is advanced in the way cancer advances when it has lots of time to spread to many areas without anyone noticing.

After working with Melissa for a few weeks, I ask her if she knew before she was diagnosed. "Were there signs? Had she ignored them?"

"No," she tells me. "I was too busy working. Building something. Having a really great life... Really great." She smiles and looks wistfully at the pictures on her walls and the accolades on her shelves. She lived the way she wanted to live. Now it is all slipping away much too quickly.

Melissa starts hospice the day after her cancer diagnosis. She is fifty years old plus two days. The cancer is incurable, inoperable. Oncology offered her palliative chemotherapy or surgery to minimize the tumor burden. There are options, Oncology told Melissa, besides hospice. The options may buy you time. There might be side effects. But there are options besides dying.

Melissa's response is a definitive no.

"Why bother having surgery or putting poison in my body when I'm going to die anyway? Sounds like a waste of the little time I have left. I want hospice. I want time with my best friend."

Kate doesn't try to convince Melissa to pursue treatment, though she tells me privately she wishes Melissa had tried. Kate wishes Melissa had given the surgeries or the chemotherapy a chance, even if it was a small one. It could be a chance to live a little longer.

But Kate loves her friend. She doesn't push her to make a decision she doesn't want to make. Kate also accepts the role of caregiver. She never once questions Melissa's desire to be with her at the end.

One day when I'm visiting, Melissa tells me there's another reason she didn't want chemo. She's known for her fabulous hair. She wanted to keep it. She knows it's vain. But she wants her hair until the end. Whenever that is.

As the weeks progress, Melissa wraps up loose ends with the business she built. She hands the keys to "the castle" over to younger, healthier people than her. She cries a lot that day. But she also wears dazzling red lipstick, a black suit, and stiletto heels. Her hair is slicked back in a sharp looking bun, not one hair out of place. She is a boss. One last time.

When Melissa becomes too weak to walk to her bathroom Kate moves her into her own home. A home outside of town, where she lives with her husband, her two kids, one dog, two cats, and a turtle. Kate cares for Melissa when she can no longer sit up on her own.

Kate is by her side when Melissa becomes so weak she has to crawl to get anywhere on her own. Kate lays down non-skid, padded rugs on the tile floors so Melissa can crawl without hurting her knees. Sometimes Melissa gets tired while crawling around the house. She lays on one of the padded rugs to nap. Kate covers her with a blanket. The dogs and turtle walk carefully around her sleeping form.

Kate washes Melissa's hair and bathes her. She combs, curls, and styles Melissa's hair to disguise the spots where it is falling out despite not doing chemo. She cleans her friend, rubs expensive lotion on her skin, and paints her nails different shades of brilliant red. She makes sure the sheets are clean and Melissa has comfortable pajamas to wear. Plus slippers and a cozy, soft robe. Kate's kids each bring Melissa a stuffed animal to keep her company in her new hospital bed on the day it is delivered by hospice.

Kate makes pureed foods from anything she can stick in a blender. She spoon-feeds Melissa when she can no longer pick up a spoon. Cereal. Carrots. Pineapple. Hamburger. Spaghetti. It all goes in the blender.

She holds Melissa and rocks her to sleep when the pain is overwhelming. Melissa cries until she finally falls asleep. Kate cries a lot too, she confides in me. But only when Melissa is not looking. She wants to be strong for Melissa, for her friend who is dying.

Hospice visits regularly. We adjust the pain medications so Melissa doesn't have to cry herself to sleep. The bath nurse comes twice a week and helps Kate with the baths as Melissa grows weaker. The chaplain visits weekly and talks with Melissa about what comes next.

Eventually Melissa is so weak she can't leave her bed to crawl. Kate asks me what she should do. What can she do.

"Is there anything left to do?" Her eyes fill with tears but don't spill over. "I've bathed her and given her medicine. She doesn't want food. Her nails are her favorite shade of red. Her pajamas and sheets are clean.... What else can I do...."

Kate turns away as the tears finally spill. She turns away from her silent, sleeping friend who is still breathing but otherwise not here. Melissa's body lays in the bed, painfully frail, shockingly pale, quietly breathing.

The unspoken question hangs in the air. Is this it? Is this the end?

I pause before answering. Knowing we can never truly predict the end, but also knowing it is near.

"There's nothing left to do. All that's left is to be. Sit and be with her, if you can. Hold her hand. Say goodbye. She's dying."

So Kate does just and only that. She holds Melissa as she breathes her last breath. She cries and cries. Saying farewell to her best friend. Her soul mate.

I feel infinitely grateful to have been given the chance to witness a window in the lives of these two loving friends. May we all be so blessed in our lives to have one true and loving friend. One true and loving friend who will do everything. One true and loving friend who is strong and caring. One true and loving friend who will sit with us when there is nothing left to be done. When all that is left is to be.

30

Turkey baster.

The referral to hospice comes in the early morning. I remember being told it was urgent. I'm sent out first thing to admit the patient to our service. "End of life" is the diagnosis. The hospice office is going to work on getting something more specific from the provider once their office opened. "End of life" gives me nothing to work with. "End of life" due to cancer is often quite different compared to "end of life" due to dementia or heart failure. I'm irritated on the drive to the house because I don't know what to expect. I can't start making a plan. I like having a plan.

I arrive at the house in the early morning. Cars are still in most driveways. Dew on the lawns and birds chirping in the trees. The sun rising low and bright in the sky. Most people still in their homes, waking up. It'll be warm today. I already feel the heat of the sun on my shoulders and back.

I knock on the door. No answer. Ring the bell. No answer. Irritation settles between my shoulder blades.

Then I hear yelling. It sounds as if it's coming from inside the house. I knock again. Still no answer. I try the doorknob. It turns easily. With some trepidation I push at the door.

"Hello?" I call out, both as greeting and warning.

The door fully opens. I freeze in the entry, on the threshold of the house. I watch a man run into the sunken living room in front of me. He is the one yelling. He's tall, slender, wearing jeans, with a half-buttoned, blue-and-yellow flannel shirt, partially tucked into the jeans. His hair is a mess. He's wearing one droopy sock.

He runs from a room I can't see, but assume must be a kitchen. He holds a turkey baster in his hand. The bulb on the end is mustard yellow. It is not November. I cannot smell turkey roasting in the house.

Another man sits, slumped, in a wheelchair, gurgling, frothing. His skin undertone is not pink, not purple, not gray, not good. *Ah, this is my patient.* He also wears a flannel shirt. Instead of jeans he's in gray sweatpants with multiple stains on them, no socks.

The sun, dew and birds are forgotten. Irritation released. This is why I'm here. End of life. All that matters now is this briefest of moments. Starting hospice and leaving hospice all in minutes time. This man in the wheelchair is actively dying. I know this instantly.

The yelling man with the turkey baster is trying to suck fluid and froth from the dying man's mouth. I have no words. Panic floods me.

How to help? What to do? This is my patient.

Then calm. A strange calm, like I've done this before. Yet I've never walked into this house. Never met these men. Never seen a turkey baster used this way. But I do know about dying.

I step across the threshold into the house. I step up and take the baster. I look at the man who holds the turkey baster.

"I can help," I tell him. "I'm with hospice." My eyes hold his long enough to make sure he sees me. His eyes are wild but they calm, slightly. He breathes heavily, wheezes a little. The man in the chair gurgles again.

"Noooo," is all the turkey-baster-man says. The word is long and drawn out. Then he crumples, deflates like an air mattress slowly leaking out. He reaches for the turkey baster I took from him.

He holds the dying man's hand in one hand, the turkey baster in his other hand. His hand is pink and warm. The dying man's hand is ashen and cold.

"I'm not ready," he says on a whisper, a sigh. *No one ever is. Ever.*

There are minutes to make a difference, any small difference. I instruct the man to help me transfer the dying man from the wheelchair to a nearby couch. The couch is brown leather and has two indentations on it. A giant colorful quilt covered in rainbows, clouds, and moons is on the back of the couch. I lay it over the dying man's thin, angular body.

I have medications to help with breathing and gurgling. I explain what I'm doing and how it will help. The meds are administered. Things smooth out. Time stretches. More moments pass. The moments feel both excruciatingly long and pitifully inadequate. *Where to begin? Do I need to explain what is sensed without words? This man is dying...he is dying now.*

I move a wooden chair from a dining table nearby so the two men can be close. One man holding the other's hand. No tears. No talking. I hear the quiet ticking of a clock somewhere in the home. The faint smell of stale coffee and something akin to burnt toast.

Then a few last shuddering breaths. And it's done. Death arrives.

Phone calls are made. Appropriate people are contacted.

Dew still glistens on the lawns and the sun remains low in the sky. I'm at the house for less than one hour. One hour of moments that will never be forgotten.

"End of life" was the diagnosis. Yes. It was.

If this had been my first visit as a hospice nurse I doubt it would have gone as smoothly. But after doing this work for a few years I found the confidence to step into a situation like this, to try to make it better in the short time we had. In this case better didn't mean preventing death, but instead providing small comforts to the dying man and his living who are left behind.

As nurses we find our rhythm and come into our own, whatever specialty we go into. And when you find that rhythm that's when you truly get to shine as a nurse. That's when you get to make countless lives better.

31

Shocks.

Zechariah is a quiet and studious man who, in his words, has led a remarkable life. Born of immigrant parents. Raised in the United States. He is the first generation to attend college. Secure a good job. Marry a wonderful woman. Raise loving, kind kids who grow up and do the same. He has many grandchildren and great grandchildren. Life has been good to him.

Life has been good to him, despite multiple heart attacks, two open heart surgeries, numerous cardiac stents, a pacemaker, ablations, and a defibrillator.

When I meet Zechariah it is in his sun-filled, book-filled, love-filled apartment. He's seated in a giant leather recliner that had duct tape holding together one arm rest. Books were piled near him on side tables, along with a hospital water bottle, a cell phone, and pictures drawn by his great grandkids. He returned home from the hospital the day before.

He is done with hospitals. He's been "in house" four times in the last four months. Each hospital stay, a little longer, each leaving him a little weaker. End stage heart failure is taking its toll. During this last hospital stay he decided it was time for hospice.

His beloved wife, devoted children, and any available grand-children are there when I arrive to meet him. This man is absolutely the center of this family. They do not want him to die, are not ready for him to die. They do not want hospice, yet they love and respect him enough to honor his wishes. They see how hard he has fought. They hear him say what a good life he's lived. Now he wants a good death.

A good death. What does that mean? For everyone it's different. For Zechariah, his big question when I arrive is what to do about his defibrillator. A defibrillator is a device that can deliver an electrical charge to the heart when the heart is in an irregular rhythm. This charge can be delivered externally with paddles or pads. The charge may also be delivered internally when a defibrillator is implanted in the chest – this is what Zechariah has.

His defibrillator is still active.

"My biggest fear is I'll die and this machine won't let me," says Zechariah as he points to the bulge in his upper left chest, just below his collarbone. "It'll shock me and shock me and not let me go." He looks at me.

"I'm ready to go. When it's my time," he says.

I nod. It's a legitimate fear. This is exactly what the device is programmed to do. Deliver a shock if a particular irregular heart rhythm is noted.

"The hospital didn't turn it off. We asked. They said they couldn't do it," Zechariah tells me. His family all nods in agreement. I nod too. *Oh boy.*

"The hospital said hospice could do it. You're hospice. This is the one thing I want," Zechariah looks at me again. His family looks at me. *Oh boy. OH BOY.*

So that's the challenge facing Zechariah and me. He's home. He doesn't want to return to the hospital again. He's ready to die when it's his time. But he has this device that may prevent him from peacefully doing that. *Oh boy. Oh boy. Oh boy.*

Once a medical device or intervention is placed, installed, or activated it can be challenging to undo or stop it. There can be great resistance to making this change. According to Zechariah and his family the hospital wasn't willing to deactivate the defibrillator. Deactivating this device won't affect Zechariah's normal, day-to-day heart rhythm. It isn't a pacemaker. Deactivating this device will prevent it from delivering a shock, or multiple shocks, when he does eventually die naturally.

In order to deactivate the defibrillator it will need to be re-programmed. I'm not trained to do this. I don't have the machine that would allow me to do this. I need a Cardiologist, or someone similar who has that training. I explain all this to Zechariah and his family. They nod.

"Great," says Zechariah, "so get me a Cardiologist!" The family all nods.

Great. Oh boy. They don't sell Cardiologists down the street. I don't have one at the office in the supply closet. Oh boy.

I try to explain that Zechariah isn't actively or imminently dying. He came home from the hospital yesterday. We'll work on getting the defibrillator deactivated this week. Our office will coordinate with a Cardiologist and we'll get it scheduled. The family nods. It sounds reasonable.

Zechariah doesn't nod. "No, this needs to be done today," he says. His family nods again. They look back at me. Reason be damned. This is his greatest concern. Therefore it's his family's greatest concern. I won't be going anywhere until this is taken care of.

Phone calls are made. Family prays in the other rooms of the house, wanting Zechariah to have the peace of knowing this is done. A Cardiologist is found, willing to come to Zechariah's apartment to help. At the end of the day the Cardiologist comes and meets with Zechariah. He meets the family. He meets me. He listens to what Zechariah wants. He listens to this quiet man who's lived a good life. He listens to Zechariah say he wants a good death.

He nods.

He opens up a small suitcase that holds a machine used for programming defibrillators. He takes care of business. Then he leaves.

Zechariah's defibrillator is now deactivated.

I say my goodbyes to Zechariah and his family. I schedule my next visit in three days. A bath nurse is scheduled to come tomorrow. A social worker will come by as well.

Zechariah holds my hand as I prepare to leave. "Thank you," he says, looking at me, eyes bright. "Thank you for the peace you have brought me and my family."

I smile back at him and nod. *You're welcome.*

"Now I shall go enjoy my dinner!" He shuffles off, holding the hands of two of his great grandchildren. I let myself out the front door.

After the Cardiologist and I leave, just like the previous night since coming home from the hospital, Zechariah eats dinner with his family. There are twenty-three people pressed in around the table.

Later, the family tells me they laughed, celebrated, and shared stories until 2 am. There was much food, much love, much laughter, much tears. Zechariah went to bed around 3 am, happy, content. He died sometime that night before 5 am when his wife woke up to go to the bathroom. He died peacefully. He died quietly. He died without any shocks.

Though I was deeply shocked when I learned of his death the next day.

Over the years of being in nursing I've learned that sometimes people sense things the rest of us can't see. Zechariah "knew" his defibrillator needed to be deactivated. He knew he couldn't peacefully let go until that was done. Then, once it was done, he quietly let go.

As a nurse we have the unusual privilege of helping people when they know what they need. Despite it being challenging (and often inconvenient) it is also generally worth the extra effort. Because in the end, as a nurse, we get to help patient's facilitate living their best possible lives. And even in this case, the best possible ending.

32

Immortality.

There are families who are wonderful storytellers. Their history and identity are woven into their stories. Stories they share about current and past situations. I had the privilege of meeting one of these families when I was caring for Ernesto. Everything was communicated in stories. The visits were long, but I looked forward to them, always finding it hard to leave. Always wanting one more story.

During a visit, I might ask Ernesto or his family if he's having pain. The answer is given as a story.

It might start with making dinner four nights ago. How Ernesto loves this particular recipe. The recipe is passed down from his grandmother to his mother to his wife to his daughter. Oh, and you don't write these recipes down. The recipe loses something if you put it on paper. The recipe's handed down by learning how to cook it in the kitchen. *Yes, yes, but what about the pain? I asked about pain...*

Now Ernesto's daughter makes the recipe. The special ingredient is a pepper. It only grows in the mountains west of the village where Ernesto grew up. Ernesto's second cousin's son ships the peppers to Ernesto's home. The peppers arrived last week. *Okay, okay, peppers. But what about pain? Is Ernesto having pain? I love this story, but pain...*

Four nights ago, Ernesto's daughter made the recipe, with the peppers. Ernesto walked. He got up on his own. He walked across the room with little support. He enjoyed a few bites of the recipe. It's one of his favorites. He sat at the big wooden table in the center of the kitchen with the family. Not in his recliner. This is how they know his pain is well-controlled. He can walk and he can eat. *Ah, there's the answer. Pain is controlled. Thank you. I love the story too. Thank you.*

For every question I ask, a story is the answer. I'm careful about how many questions I ask.

Ernesto is head of the family. An immigrant who crossed borders, then made a life for himself in this country. He met his wife here. They married and had three kids, one survived. It was a hard life, his wife tells me, but worth it. They became citizens here. They learned the language. They learned new customs. They built their own home. This is the home where I meet him and all his family. I learn all of this as I ask about his skin and if he has any rashes or sores. I ask about sleep habits and bowel movements. All the answers come with stories. Their history and identity are woven into the answers.

"Ernesto, are you having problems with swallowing," I ask during a visit.

Ernesto doesn't answer often due to his advancing dementia and English being a second language. His daughter answers this time.

"Well," she starts, then pauses. "There was the one time we had a pig roast in the backyard." Ernesto's daughter gestures to the patio beyond the sliding glass doors.

"We roasted the pig for three days. It was hot out there. We had watermelon eating contests with the kids," his daughter continues.

The rest of the family nods along. *Yes, but what about swallowing? How does this relate to swallowing?*

"So Papi and Mami decide to join the watermelon eating contest..."

Papi? Mami?

I have to interrupt. "Who's Papi? Who's Mami?" I ask.

Ernesto's daughter gestures to Ernesto, who nods. *Ah, that's Papi.*

"His wife must be Mami?" I ask. The family nods again. Ernesto smiles, perhaps recognizing the name.

His daughter picks up the story again.

"So, Papi and Mami join the eating contest after shoving in their teeth. Papi's having a horrible time with watermelon shooting out his mouth. He's bellowing. He's grunting. Everyone else is done. We can't figure it out..." the rest of the family nods along as she tells the story. They smile. Ernesto smiles. They know how this ends. *Swallowing... don't forget the swallowing...*

"Papi finally takes out the fake teeth and thunks 'em down in front of Mami. Then they look at each other and start howling with laughter. No one knows what's going on," says his daughter. The family all nod and smile again. They've heard this story before.

"It turns out they mixed up their teeth. Papi couldn't eat a thing," his daughter's eyes sparkle as she finishes. I smile and nod. Everyone laughs. *I love this story, like all the others... But swallowing...?*

Once the laughter dies down, his daughter picks the story again. "Papi's teeth stopped fitting a few weeks ago. We started blending and mushing all his food. He swallows fine now. No more choking or coughing." *Ah, swallowing! There we are.*

I smile. "Thank you. That's helpful. Keep doing what you're doing. Sounds like it's working well. Please let me know if he starts choking again or aspirates food."

So the visits go. One question. Many stories. Repeat again.

Could the visits be faster? Absolutely.

Do I want them to be? Absolutely not.

I've been doing this work long enough to know it's important to listen to the stories. It's important to ask my questions and do my work, but it's equally important to listen. Bear witness. I provide the healthcare. The family provides the soul care, the stories.

This family knows Ernesto is slowly dying. They know he'll not be here much longer. I'm a reminder of that when I come to visit them in their home. So they share their stories with me. They relive pieces of Ernesto's life with him still here. Celebrating him.

The stories don't stop his death from coming. He still dies after about six months in hospice. He dies, but he also lives on. In the stories.

I believe there's an immortality that comes with the sharing of stories. The kind of stories that are passed down from generation to generation or from friend to friend. The stories (hopefully) outlive the person who lived them. In those stories the person now lives on.

Perhaps there's a lesson or two to be learned here. Share your stories. Humans have a long, rich tradition of passing things down through oral traditions - sharing stories. To tell the tales and reminisce. But also, live your life so it is worthy of telling stories about.

33

Puzzles.

Abe and Paulina have been married for "decades upon decades," in their words. Abe is in hospice for end-stage many things. Paulina care for him as only a wife ("who still loves him," her words, not mine) can do after decades of marriage. Abe and Paulina live with a menagerie of dogs, cats, and birds. Evidence is scattered throughout their home of children, grandchildren, great grandchildren. Photos, hand-drawn pictures, craft projects, homemade gifts are on every horizontal surface. Noise and love linger in every corner, along with sticky fingerprints on the walls.

Abe and Paulina live outside the big city in an unassuming home on a beautiful piece of land near the ocean. I can hear the not-so-distant waves crashing when it's quiet. The house is brick, painted ocher, built into the landscape. It's surrounded by palm trees, lemon trees, and bougainvillea in rich, saturated pinks, oranges, yellows. It smells like fresh cut grass and salt water all the time.

Abe and Paulina raised their family in this home. They planned to grow old together in this home. But life doesn't always allow you your plans. Abe is dying. And it's too soon for both of them.

"It's three decades too early," he tells me one day during a routine hospice visit. "We should have more time." He gazes at Paulina's eyes then the sky. Both are crystalline blue.

She walks over and holds his wrinkled, withered hand. He sighs and rubs her hand against his hollowed cheek. Closing his eyes, tears run silently down his cheeks.

Meeting Abe and Paulina the first time, I have no idea they "escaped" from his country decades earlier. Why would I know that? They tell me their story in pieces over many visits.

Abe and Paulina met at a café. It was known for its coffee and puzzles. A simple café in a large, sprawling, ancient city with many cafés, all known for good coffee. *How did they both end up at this one café? How did they learn to communicate? How did they see past all that was forbidden?*

"Love," they tell me after I ask them my questions, "and maybe some luck. And one of our Gods or both."

As I listen to Abe's lungs and heart, Paulina holds his pale, fragile hand in hers. The way they gaze at each other, it feels as if they are still falling in love. I can picture them forty years ago.

Abe does his work and drinks coffee in the café. The café is somewhere between his office and where he lives. Paulina is visiting his country with her parents. She stops at the café somewhere between where she is going and where she is staying. She needed something to pass the time that didn't involve speaking a language she couldn't speak very well. She can drink strong coffee and do puzzles.

One afternoon they meet. Neither can tell me any real details, except about the puzzle. It was a picture of a mountain.

On that day Abe sits at his table, does his work, and covertly watches Paulina piece together the puzzle. Paulina sits at her table, sips her coffee, and covertly watches Abe work.

After that day Abe keeps coming back hoping to see Paulina. And he does his work.

Paulina keeps coming back to drink more coffee, finish more puzzles. And to see Abe.

Somehow they connect. They learn to speak to each other.

They fall in love.

Abe is not supposed to leave his country. Paulina can leave freely, any time. If they stay in Abe's country they can't be married. If they flee the country they might be caught, imprisoned, or worse.

They flee.

In separate trains into the night. With only their hopes they will meet days later in another country. On a different continent hundreds of miles away. They plan to meet at a train station on a predetermined platform. They'll wait for each other until they're both there. They'll wait for as long as they need to wait. This was in a time when cell phones and email did not exist.

It takes three weeks. Twenty-one days.

Paulina arrives after seven days.

For the next two weeks Paulina lives at this train station. Trying to look like she belongs. Trying to fit in. Not call attention to herself. Waiting. Hoping. Abe arrives two weeks later. I can only imagine how long those three weeks felt for both of them. How joyous their reunion on that platform must have been. How deep the breath they each took when they finally saw each other again. Such relief.

They leave the train station together. With one bag of belongings between the two of them to start their new life together. They also carried a lot of hope and love with them, they tell me.

When they met they didn't speak a shared language. Now they both speak at least three shared languages.

When they met they didn't practice the same religion. They still don't.

When they met it was forbidden for them to be together. Yet here they are. Together.

I learn all of some of these amazing details as I check Abe's skin. Listen to his lungs, heart, and abdomen. Answer questions about appetite changes. Discuss bowel movements. Review logs Paulina keeps of Abe's pain levels and what medications they're using to manage it.

Sometimes it feels like they're telling me a made-up story, a plot line, a movie script. But here they are, living proof of what can happen when you're young, in love and determined.

And now, decades later their house still has at least one puzzle in progress on a table. Always.

When I visit Abe, Paulina often prepares strong, bitter coffee while I take care of the healthcare business. There's plenty of work to be done making sure Abe is comfortable. Addressing changes and issues that arise as he creeps closer to the end of his life. The work of nursing happens, interwoven with the stories. The stories are the beautiful gift that comes with being able to practice healthcare and be present at the same time. Doing and being.

When the work is done Paulina and I sit at the puzzle table while Abe dozes on the couch, bed or hammock. I take an extra ten to fifteen minutes to drink coffee and sit with them, while we work on a puzzle. This time I spend being with them, is also how I learn much of their beautiful story about their unexpected love. Piece by piece it falls into place.

Whenever I sit down to work on a puzzle today, I think of Abe and Paulina. Their story lives on in this small way.

34

DNR.

When I meet Odelia she is well past her hundredth birthday. She's been in hospice for about a year, slowly declining. Her previous nurse left our practice. I am her newly assigned nurse. I park my car and walk up to her home for my first visit.

Upon arriving, I quickly notice a pink, laminated sign on her black metal mailbox. "DNR" is printed in large block letters on hot pink paper. Her name and house number are on the box as well, but the DNR dwarfs both.

There's a DNR sign on her front door. Same large block letters and hot pink paper. Odelia briskly opens the door after my second knock. She is pulling on a hot pink bathrobe. Odelia is less than five feet tall and has spiky white hair with random tufts of hot pink throughout. *Whoa.*

"Hello," I say, introducing myself, extending my hand, and explaining why I'm there.

She shakes my hand firmly and welcomes me into her home. I note three more DNR signs in her entryway. Same message, same block letters, same hot pink paper. DNR.

DNR means "**D**o **N**ot **R**esuscitate." In the medical world it means if someone stops breathing or their heart stops beating you do not resuscitate them. No rescue breathing. No CPR (cardiopulmonary resuscitation).

Okay. I will not be doing CPR. Or rescue breathing. Or calling 911. DNR.

As I enter the house Odelia scampers down the wide tile hallway towards a kitchen at the far end of the house. She beckons me to follow.

I find two more DNR signs posted along the hallway. They're sandwiched in between oversized woven wall hangings, plants, and bookshelves stuffed with children's books. There are small pillows on the floor next to the bookshelves. The pillows feel like an open invitation to sit down and read. I feel at-home here.

The hallway opens into a giant kitchen forgotten in the mid-1970s. As I follow Odelia into the kitchen, rust orange, lime green, macramé planters with hanging plants, and dark brown tiles assault my senses. On the stove, on top of one burner, sits a giant silver pot with steam billowing out of it. Odelia ably climbs up a step stool that's standing on the floor. She sticks her head into the steam cloud.

Odelia's head pokes back out and she blinks twice. "Might as well make yourself useful," she tells me. She points to the stool she is currently standing on. "I need to move this now."

As I walk around the countertop to reach her and the stool I find two more DNR signs taped on kitchen cabinets. Odelia climbs off the stool and points to a spot on the floor in front of the kitchen sink. She directs me to move the stool there.

Not knowing what else to do, I pick up the stool and move it.

Before I have a chance to object or help, Odelia hefts the giant, steaming pot off the burner. She carries it over to the sink. She climbs up the step stool and proceeds to dump the contents of the pot into a massive straining dish that fills the entire sink. Bright pink water splashes everywhere. The steam clears and I see the strainer overflowing with red beets.

The pink tufts of hair become clear as Odelia picks up a beet. She looks at it then sets it back down. She runs her hand through her hair. More pink tufts appear. Magic. *I want pink tufts...*

"You're my new hospice nurse." A statement, not a question, as she looks away from her beets and focuses on me.

"Yup...." I look back and wait. This is not my first time doing this. I wait for her to continue. I know better than to rush in with my own agenda.

"Good. Here's what I want. I give everyone the same spiel," her eyes focus on mine to make sure I'm paying attention. I am.

"I do not, I repeat, *do not*, want to be resuscitated. I've lived a *wonderful* life but it's time when it's time. I have no family, no kids. No one left. So. No CPR. No zapping me. No tubes. No prolonging things. You let me go. You make sure everyone who comes on this property and into this house with hospice knows that. Got it?" A hot pink finger points my direction. Pink tufts of hair stick out all over. *I love this woman.*

I nod. "Yup," I reply. I look around the kitchen finding another two DNR signs on the refrigerator. "I'm pretty sure all your signs might help with that too..." I gesture at the DNR sign closest to me on the cabinet. I smile.

She looks at me. Then she snorts and says we'll get along just fine. She pats my arm leaving a hot pink mark. Magic.

I'm blessed to be given a few lovely months with Odelia before she dies. I visit her weekly. I lose count of how many DNR signs she has. If there's a record for having the most DNR signs she would win.

Odelia was always busy doing something. She made most of her own food. Cleaned her own house. Paid her own bills. She had a caregiver help with driving and shopping once a week. Otherwise she was independent at over-one-hundred-years old. She walked daily. Laid in the sun daily (often wearing no clothes). Took a bubble bath daily.

She read voraciously with giant reading glasses. I did get to sit on the pillows and read children's books with her occasionally. One of my favorite memories is of Odelia sitting on a large, crumpled brown pillow, reading "Where the Wild Things Are" to me. While wearing her hot pink bathrobe and huge reading glasses. She was pure joy. Magic.

Odelia played piano. She knit, wove, and crocheted. She loved infomercials. She thought the new inventions were delightful. Occasionally she bought one for $19.95 plus S&H (shipping and handling), then proudly demonstrated it for me. The most memorable was a small gadget that lit up different colors and was supposed to help reduce pain. She thought the blue lights helped most with her knee pain. The green lights were great for her sciatica.

Odelia died quietly in her home. She transitioned quickly and with very little fuss. There was no CPR. I'm grateful we were able to give her that. Considering how much joy she gave anyone who came to visit her.

Of note, she died holding a small jar of beets. I've always wondered if she found a way to take those beets with her into her next life. I've also decided when my hair goes fully white or gray I will boil beets and create my own pink highlights in memory of Odelia. Magic.

35

The postman.

My patient was a retired postman. He knew every address, every house, every family in his middle-of-America-small-town. He can tell me the names of every person who lived there regardless of whether or not they received mail. In the mornings, he ate eggs and bacon, coffee black, no cream or sugar, at the local diner. He walked his route while chatting with whomever he came across, adults, kids, dogs. It didn't matter. He came back to the diner for lunch. Best hamburger or club sandwich or mac-and-cheese and yes, he would take an extra serving of fries, no-thank-you no-salad-today. He would chat and visit some more. Then he would finish his route. Head home and clean up.

He coached baseball and cheered for the local high school football team. He served pancakes at fundraisers. He bought a chocolate bar from every kid who ever approached him even though he didn't like chocolate. He had drawers full of uneaten chocolate bars. He saw families leave his town for bigger towns. His mail route got smaller. His son didn't come back home after college. His son stayed west.

The postman was moved to a giant white house on the cliff about one year before I met him. He "got moved," he told me, when he started spending more time in the hospital than at home. He was still working as a postman or at least trying too. But he was "uprooted", by his son and the good intentions of doctors, both in his town and where his son lived. They all thought he could have a better life if he moved out west with his son.

The postman's son had done very well in his industry. So when his dad needed more care, he moved his dad from middle-of-America-small-town to his white house on the cliffs over the sparkling water. The son hired 24-hour caregivers. The postman was given a private suite of rooms with his own entrance. He has decks on each side of the white house. The postman can watch the sun rise or set from his dual decks.

Now the postman lives on top of the ocean. And he is starting hospice. To reach the white house on the cliff I turn off the main highway onto a poorly marked two-lane road. The road eventually turns into a gravel one-lane road, ultimately becoming little more than a goat trail. In the spring it's pure magic driving up the mountainside. All wildflowers in orange, pink, and yellow, plus tall green grass, blue sky, and turquoise ocean. The house is white, all windows, and shiny glass. Perched on the edge of a cliff with views of mountains and sea.

It seems beyond ideal to me. The house. The caregivers. The views.

What more could someone possibly want? What a perfect life.

The postman is taken to specialists for his "ticker" and told he can't eat bacon or eggs or hamburgers. He has to exercise and eat salads and at eighty-plus-years old he has to retire. Oh and no more beer. And no more cigarettes. And no, you can't go back to work and deliver the post. Nor can you go home again. And look at this beautiful house and view and twenty-four-hour care. We'll make sure you're comfortable and take you to all the best doctors. We'll keep you here and alive and make sure you're safe. Safe and well. Safe and cared for. Safe.

The postman and I, once I get to know him and he gets to know me, we settle into a rhythm.

I visit his new home at least weekly. We chat while I rewrap his legs, because he has sores and they weep. He tells me stories as I look at his ankles. I listen to his stories and his heart and his lungs. I ask him questions about his appetite, his weight, his bowel movements. He opens up more, once he realizes I am not reporting everything we talk about to his son.

One day he surprises me. One day he tells me his truth. I'm wrapping his legs and nearly finished with our visit.

"I hope my ticker just stops," he drawls at me. "Just stops..." He looks outside at the sparkling turquoise waters.

"Hmmm," I respond, not sure how to respond but not wanting to shut him down. I'll miss this man and his stories of home and beer and brats.

"This isn't livin' ya know... Not this...," he gestures around at the soy milk and granola on his side table. Waiting to be eaten for breakfast. The hand weights and medicine ball in the corner, to be used with his personal trainer. The views of mountains and oceans. The tall white walls, soaring ceilings, and glass windows.

"Not my kind of livin'," he drawls and nods. I smile sadly.

I suppose it's not. But I thought it was paradise...I thought you had everything...

As I grab more gauze wraps from my medical bag I ask him to tell me about his kind of living.

"My kind of livin'... I'm not hungry." Another gesture at the soy and granola concoction.

He continues, "not alone all day, exceptin' the people who work here. The people who's paid to be here." A wave of his arm encompasses the house, the corner with the training equipment, the immaculate bathroom, and the bed, already made.

He sighs, "it's nice, I s'pose." He gets quiet. I wait. Finish wrapping his legs. Sit down in a chair across from him.

"I miss my home." He sounds small and the word 'home' feels heavy, like it's carrying every one of his eighty-plus-years. Home. Like it's carrying every loss he's suffered in the past year. Home.

"This... is not home." His head shakes back and forth. "Nuh-uhhh ma'am." Rheumy eyes focus on me. He smiles a little. But it's a sad smile.

"I'm grateful you know... Well, I know I *should* be grateful. And I am." He nods.

Is he trying to convince himself or me?

My idea of paradise is shattering.

Maybe the house on the hill and 24-hour care and safety are not all they're cracked up to be.

"I'm grateful to be alive. To be safe." He says these things like he's reciting from a book. I wonder how many times a day he says these words out loud. I wonder how much he actually believes them. Sadness encircles my heart. Heavy, damp sadness. You are a*live. You are safe. But at what cost?*

I wish I could take you away from here. To a small apartment in middle-of-America. You could eat bacon. Drink black coffee. Order a second serving of fries. Visit with the people you know. The people who became your family when you had no family left in your town. You knew all their names. Even if they didn't receive mail. You knew them and could say hi to them. They said hi back.

I say none of this out loud though.

The postman takes my free hand as I start to pack up my medical bag. He holds my hand and looks at me with his wobbly smile. His hands are covered in scars and small brown spots, veins popping out here and there. They look like worn pieces of driftwood. His hands wrap around mine. His skin is soft and cool. I hold very still.

"I know I'm lucky to be kept alive an' all... but mostly, I jus' feel kept."

Then he stares out the windows again, holding my one hand in his for a bit longer.

We sit together above the sparkling waters. We sit together in companionable silence, contemplating what he has just said. Sit together in a place that seems like it should be paradise but perhaps is a bit closer to prison.

36

Mystery man.

The house is immense. The room Mr. Lee's in, is the largest of all the rooms I see. A hospital bed is placed in the center of the substantial room, below the central beam of the peaked ceiling. It faces a giant picture window that looks out onto the mountains. The ceiling and walls are all dark paneled wood. No lights in the room, just very large windows on two sides. Mr. Lee lays in the center of the bed. The rest of the room is completely austere – no clutter, no knick-knacks, no dust, no bunnies. No clues about this man who lays in the bed, breathing comfortably and slowly. This man who's on hospice.

There is a single folding chair set next to the bed and a clean, white water bottle. A single caregiver stands without moving at the side of the bed, watching what I'm doing as I listen to Mr. Lee's heart and lungs. Lub-dub. Whoosh-whoosh. Lub-dub. Whoosh-whoosh.

Unzipping my medical bag to get a piece of equipment feels like I'm shouting an obscenity into the quiet space as it breaks the endless silence. I apologize reflexively. Then feel bad for breaking the silence again with an apology. The entire room is silent. The entire house. All noise absorbed by the sheer size, the soft tan carpet, and something else I can't quite put my finger on. The entire house is devoid of smell. No cleaning products, no cooking, no baking, no dust or must or anything that would give my senses a place to settle.

My sock-clad feet leave prints when I walk to the center of the room to meet Mr. Lee. Impressions left on the floor, that someone was here. Someone walked here, in this immense house. Me. This is not just a bed floating in the middle of an impressive, quiet room.

Where are the footprints from the caregiver? From Mr. Lee? Does he ever get out of bed? Where's the bathroom? He has to get up and move sometime. How is the carpet so untouched? I have the eerie feeling I have entered an alternate dimension or something that is not quite of this world.

I ask many of my usual questions. Mr. Lee answers quietly in single word whispers.

"Are you having any pain or discomfort?"

"Comfortable."

"Do you have any questions about hospice or what is happening?"

"Understand."

"Is there anything you need in terms of additional support or supplies?"

"Nothing."

"Do you have any questions you'd like to ask me? Anything we haven't discussed today?"

"No."

Usually people do. He does not.

I ask the caregiver my questions. He answers with the same single word whispers. He also doesn't have any questions for me. There's nothing left to do.

I pad quietly out of the room. Into the long hallway, back to the entryway to retrieve my shoes. My shoes are the only shoes there. I hope they don't leave dirt or smudges on the seemingly untouched floors.

Why are there no smells? No sounds? Just a really clean, giant house and two people in it, from what I can see.

I never see another person during my journeys in and out of this sizable house. There are no paintings on the wood paneled walls, no photographs, no sculptures. The hallway is wood paneled on one side, wooden doors blend in, making the long wall appear to be seamless. Glass windows line the other side running parallel to the same mountain range Mr. Lee looks at from his bed. The hallway is at least ten feet wide with no scratches on the immaculate wooden floors. No clues here about this man and the life he lived (is living). Except that everything is exceptionally clean, quiet, and odorless.

Each weekly visit is the same. He has no questions. The caregiver has no questions. They both whisper. I live in fear of burping or worse, passing gas. *How far would that sound travel? And what about the smell? Oh gosh.* I start unzipping my medical bag in the car before I come in, just to have one less noise disturb the space.

I make a point to remember clean, hole-less socks on the days I'm scheduled to visit.

Who is this man? Who is this caregiver? Is there anyone else in this house? What are their stories? How did they get here? Does Mr. Lee have family? Friends? Where are the other people? Why are there no other footprints on the carpet?

I have questions. But I don't ask them, realizing it would be inappropriate.

Mr. Lee dies on a Wednesday. I'm called to come out. I listen to his chest. I nod to the caregiver. Yes, he's died. The caregiver stands quietly at the head of the bed. The room looks as it always does. The bed in the center. Soft tan untouched carpet. The only footprints are mine. One folding chair. One white water bottle. Windows looking out at nature.

The mortuary is called. They arrive quickly. They do their task efficiently. I'm grateful to see they leave footprints on the carpet (it's not just me). Mr. Lee's body is taken away. I wonder if his soul is gone too. I never gained a sense of who this man was. I turn to say goodbye to the caregiver.

He whispers, "good-bye," then sheds one single solitary tear. It runs down his cheek and drops onto the tan carpet. The image of that single tear has haunted me. So many unanswered questions.

Mr. Lee and this caregiver remain in my memories. I learned so little about them. I was unable to connect with either, in the way I like to connect. I did my job the best I could and respected the privacy they seemed to require. Sometimes that is the best we can do as nurses. Be extremely proficient. Don't force a connection. Don't pry.

In the world today I suppose I could search for Mr. Lee's name and find all sorts of information, but I choose not to do this. Mr. Lee volunteered nothing about himself. I choose to respect that. He'll always remain a mystery, this man in this bed in the middle of this large room with a single caregiver and a silent, spotless house.

37

Let's get started.

When I meet Wilma she's in her early nineties and mad-as-hell she's still alive. She's ill, but not ill enough (in her words). She has just enough money to afford her apartment plus a caregiver for part of the day, but not enough (according to her). She's tired, but not enough to stop waking up every day (her words not mine). She's angry, but not enough to do anything about anything (also her words). Wilma is mad, tired, and angry.

At my first visit with Wilma I tell her I'm the nurse from hospice. She brightens considerably. This doesn't happen very often.

"Oh," she says, "someone is finally here to do something about this life I don't want anymore. Good. How do we get started?"

I'll never forget the smile on her face. The utter confusion I felt about her obvious excitement.

"Get started?" I ask, wondering what she thinks I'm going to do with her.

I'm not going to cause you to die right now. You know that right? That's not what hospice is.

Unfortunately, she answers, "yes! With dying of course. How do I get started? I'd prefer to start right now. Thank you." She nods her head and smiles. *Oh boy.* This woman thinks I am going to help her die immediately. *Nope. That's not what I do. And she said thank you!? Very oolite about it.*

Wilma is desperately ready to die. She's at a point in her life where she feels everything is done. She's not suicidal. She's probably depressed. She doesn't feel she has a reason to still be here, to be living. *But you are living... So live for goodness sake. Live.*

On the days I come to see Wilma it's often around lunch time. She eats lunch and I check her vital signs. I check her skin, because she has sores. We play cribbage. She tells me stories of the life she liked, not the one she has now. She often asks me, "when does it begin, the dying, when? When does the final party start?"

I tell her death and dying are unpredictable. Kind of like life. I tell her she might as well live as long as she can. She beats me at cribbage. Another day passes. *The dying, it comes soon enough. But for now, you get to live.*

With hospice Wilma has a bath nurse who sees her twice a week. Her skin sores get better. A chaplain comes once a week. They discuss whatever Wilma wants to discuss about life, death, and everything in between. A social worker helps her get the papers in order. She has many complaints about "the papers," but that gets better once they're in order. Wilma gains weight. She gains strength. She becomes less ill.

The dying, the thing she wants most, does not start.

She tells me, every time I see her, she's mad-as-hell at me because she's still living. Now she is actually living more, not dying. Then she annihilates me at cribbage. Another day passes.

Eventually Wilma becomes so much less ill she "graduates" from hospice. On that day she is really mad-as-hell because I haven't done what she asked. She has not died. *You have lived. You are living.*

Instead the exact opposite happened. And even after she's discharged from hospice services I continue to visit her once a month for lunch, cribbage, stories, and a tongue-lashing about being alive. The bath nurse stops by to say 'hello' even though she no longer gives her a bath. The chaplain visits as well.

With hospice, Wilma started talking to people, besides her part-time caregiver. She suddenly had four more people in her life coming to see her regularly. Life became less dark. The days became less long. Loneliness was replaced by stretches of being alone, but not lonely. Soul care.

Her skin healed. She gained weight. She became stronger. She walked more. Healthcare.

She shared her stories. She shared meals with people. She laughed. She beat me at cribbage nearly every time we played. She found a bit of meaning to being alive a bit longer. I think with help from the hospice chaplain or social worker she may have even reconnected with old friends in the area. Her social network exponentially grew and her willingness to live seemed to grow with it.

Wilma lived another ten years after she first asked me, "how do we get started?"

Eventually she did die, ten years after originally being placed on hospice. Now that she is no longer mad-as-hell at me, I miss her dearly.

You got to live though Wilma. Before you died. You got to live.

38

Tea time.

Lydia spoke five languages fluently by the time she was twenty. She spent most of her adult life speaking English. She thinks French is the most beautiful. She likes to write in German. As she aged and her mind slipped she switched more often between the languages. Sometimes a conversation would start in English and she would answer in German, then start singing in French. She was in her nineties when I met her.

Lydia always dressed up when she knew I was coming to visit. Sometimes that meant she wore a bathrobe with her nightdress. Sometimes it meant a moth-ball-smelling ball gown pulled out of a box. Occasionally she was in slacks and a sweater. Her lipstick was bright red and always crooked. Always. She often forgot to draw on her left eyebrow. Lydia had tea and cookies ready whenever I walked in the door. The cookies were small and round. The tea was strong and black.

We drink tea and I ask her the questions I need to ask and do her physical exam.

"Do you have pain?"

"No dear."

"How has your blood pressure been?"

"Fine dear."

"Are you sleeping well?"

"Yes dear."

"How's your appetite?"

"Good, eat another cookie dear. I'll eat one too. See! My appetite is fine."

"Do you have questions about hospice?"

"No dear."

"Do you have anything you want to discuss today that we haven't covered yet?"

"Yes, but it has nothing to do with hospice. When are you going to get married dear? I have a great-nephew in New York. He'd be perfect. He's got a good job. You'd like him," she states while patting my leg and winking at me.

The goal is to keep her as comfortable as we can without compromising her clarity. Staying sharp is important to Lydia. How else can she beat the pants off her son-in-law when they play bridge? She prefers to have a little pain and greater clarity than the other way around.

Sometimes she plays the piano for me. She sings quietly to herself. Often in German. It sounds like lullabies. Between the tea, the cookies, and the singing I sometimes forget I'm working. I always do the work, but am able to enjoy time with Lydia too.

Over tea one day, Lydia tells me she escaped from Germany decades earlier in a hay cart. Her sister was lying under the hay next to her. Their parents didn't come with them. Their brother didn't make the trip. They're sent into the countryside. In the night. With the clothes they're wearing, a loaf of bread, a few meager coins, and passage on a ship that leaves England in two weeks. They come to America with nothing but their religion, their dreams, and each other.

In America Lydia blooms. She becomes an architect and designs the house in which I visit her. She plays piano. She could have made a career of either. Instead she married, she tells me. She raises children. She sees her husband die and her sister. She sees one friend after another pass away. She's the only person she knows who speaks German anymore. Until her granddaughter started learning it at school. This makes her smile. Her granddaughter speaks German now.

Until the day she dies Lydia is always gracious, kind, and welcoming. On the day she dies she is peaceful, laying in her bed in a blue nightgown with a fan running on low in the background.

There are so many people she misses. So many people she hopes she will see again. Lydia believes the afterlife will be a great, grand party. She'll be able to smoke again. She always tells me she misses that. Drinking a highball and smoking long, skinny cigarettes. While wearing a gown and high heels. Her lips painted red, and eyebrows drawn on in small dark lines. On the day she tells me this, she's wearing a velvet bathrobe and missing one eyebrow. Yet I can still picture her glammed up with a cocktail in one hand, sitting on the edge of a piano bench. I remind her smoking isn't good for her health. She laughs and pats my arm.

Lydia tells me jokes in different languages, then laughs so hard she snorts tea up her nose. I laugh because she's laughing and snorting. This is how most of our visits go. Tea. Laughter. Stories. Singing. Jokes. With a dash of healthcare mixed in between.

I believe the laughter, sharing time, and telling stories contribute to why she lives ten months longer than anyone predicted. Having known her only briefly I wish it could have been ten years. Or twenty. Or a lifetime.

Meeting Lydia was a gift. I can never repay the universe for the gift it was to know her. I can only share part of her story. I can hope other people she touched in her life felt as blessed as I did. Her prognosis was grim when I met her, one to two months or less remaining. But hospice services came in and helped stabilize things. Regular nurse visits. Regular home health aide visits with baths and skin care. Visits from a chaplain and a social worker. It all helps.

This is one of the things I love about hospice. Sometimes (not always, but sometimes) when a few extra people are added to the care team there's a little more laughter, purpose and tea (with cookies). It may make a world of difference, all the world.

Death still comes. It's still painful and hard but perhaps it's also less dark and bleak because there's so much more living mixed in at the end as well, not just dying. I hope Lydia is now enjoying her grand party in a gown with shockingly high shoes. She's drinking and smoking (despite medical advice to the contrary). Telling stories and playing piano. And laughing so hard so she snorts. I hope the laughter and joy only keep growing.

39

Jokes.

When I meet Harvey his brain is too far gone for him to tell me his own name, his birthdate, or where he is. But we instantly connect when he pulls out a chair and asks me to sit as he pats the seat and smiles a big gummy smile at me.

He vigorously shakes my hand to introduce himself. "I'm..." he says, then trails off, unable to remember his own name. He eventually finishes with, "I'm me." Then he smiles and chuckles, pats his belly, and we move on with the visit. Harvey still has a few jokes he tells but the joke and the punchlines never match up. I assume it's due to his advanced dementia.

Harvey lives in a memory care home with locked doors, security gates, and round-the-clock care. You see he is incredibly adept at getting through locks and gates and walls and caregivers. But he is no longer very adept at getting dressed or reading street signs or finding his way home.

His wife of over sixty years comes to visit him nearly every day. Harvey smiles and nods at her when she arrives. If he remembers she's coming to visit, he puts on a lopsided bow tie with his white t-shirt and sweatpants. Harvey makes sure she has the best chair in the room, a padded one with armrests. (Those are his favorite chairs too.) Harvey sits next to her and lets her read to him. Paperback novels she buys for a dollar at the local Goodwill store. Patterson. Higgins Clark. Steele. Evanovich. The authors and genres vary widely. They seem to enjoy them all equally.

She tells Harvey all the stories and updates about people he doesn't quite remember any longer. While she talks, Harvey holds her hand and smiles. Sometimes he hums or whistles. Nothing recognizable but always a tune that gets stuck in my head for the rest of the day. And I carry a little bit of Harvey with me wherever I go, sometimes humming the tune as well.

Harvey and his wife share a soft-serve, ice cream in the afternoons or a piece of chocolate cake if she's there in the evenings. Harvey always walks her to the door to make sure she gets to her car alright. Then staff escort him back inside.

As a hospice nurse, I'm a new person coming into the home (or in this case the care facility). I never know how someone with dementia or memory loss will receive me. But with Harvey it's like we're old friends or family. He stands up and hugs me when I arrive. He asks me to sit with him. I suspect I remind him of someone in his past that he still remembers. We get along well.

As I do the work I come to do, checking blood pressure, looking at his skin, listening to his belly, he tells me rambling stories of his work, kids, dogs. Harvey liked to tinker with clocks. He liked to dance with his wife. He liked to tell jokes. He regularly tells me three or four each visit. Because he laughs at his jokes I end up laughing too – laughter often spreads.

The only times Harvey is not gentle are when infections set in – a bladder infection, an upper respiratory infection, an infected skin wound. He becomes aggressive and surly. Not himself. The staff know there's an infection somewhere. They call hospice. The infection is treated. Harvey returns to telling jokes and chuckling softly to himself. Sharing soft serve with his wife in the afternoons. Sitting in the sun and dozing.

Harvey dies in his sleep in the middle of the week about six months after I meet him. Gentle and uneventful, without any warning. Although I suppose nine decades of living, being in hospice, a history of four heart attacks, and fourteen coronary stents could be considered warnings of sorts.

I have the privilege of being invited to attend his memorial service. I hear stories of his life told by his family and friends. The people he left behind talk about his kindness and generosity. His love for his wife, his family, and his dogs. I'm nervous going to the service but also honored to be included.

Harvey's sons talk about Harvey telling jokes. It turns out he *never* matched the jokes with the punchlines. Ever. And he always chuckled about it. And his sons always laughed too. So did his friends. So did anyone Harvey ever told a joke to. It was his way. He could make people laugh.

I feel blessed to have met Harvey. He reminds me that even with dementia, even with memory loss, we may still be ourselves. The person we are at our very core. We may not remember our name, how to put on pants, or use a spoon, but we are still human. We are still connected in other ways.

So in honor of Harvey, a joke. But first, please imagine a soft chuckling ninety-year-old man wearing a navy sweater vest over a white t-shirt and gray sweatpants. Bright pink sneakers on both feet. Frizzy white hair above both ears but nowhere else on his shiny bald head. He smiles a gummy smile with no teeth. His eyes crinkle and shine with the joy of telling jokes.

Harvey: Knock knock

Me: Who's there?
Harvey: Banana
Me: Banana who?
Harvey: The bunny, the rabbi, and Santa Claus.
(Soft chuckling ensues.)

40

Bruce.

At two am my pager goes off. I'm awakened from a deep sleep. When I call in, the operator tells me the wife who called in thinks her husband is actively dying. He, the husband, is comfortable. But she, the wife, is nervous about being alone when it happens. I'm dressed, in my car, and on the road, in just under ten minutes. I arrive at their home within thirty minutes of the page.

I've never met this family but have some familiarity due to our weekly group hospice meetings. Liver failure diagnosed a few months ago. He opted to pursue palliative care and enjoy the time he had remaining. Hospice was called in about a month ago.

I introduce myself to the wife. I let the patient know I'm there but he's too far gone to the other side to acknowledge. I also meet the family dog, Bruce, an ancient basset hound with bloodshot red eyes and droopy ears. He circles between my legs over and over, doing figure-eights.

Bruce keeps moving and can't seem to sit still. The wife sits in a folding chair and holds her husband's hand. I fade into the background as much as I can while time passes and the end comes. The husband dies peacefully about thirty minutes after I arrived. The wife calls the mortuary. Then we wait. Bruce continues to pace and circle. Pace and circle.

It's a mild night and the sky is clear with as many stars as can be expected in a developed area. The back door of the house is open to a porch. The scent of jasmine and damp earth waft inside. Palm trees rustle in the breeze. A sprinkler comes on nearby. I can smell the water. The night is peaceful except for Bruce.

Bruce is now circling from the porch to the room where the husband passed away. Then from the room to the wingback chair, where the wife sits stoically waiting for the mortuary. Next from the wife's chair to my legs to make his figure-eight circles around them. Then repeat. Over and over, as if Bruce is powered by a battery that will never give out. Porch, room. Room, chair. Chair, legs. Repeat.

Bruce does laps. The breeze rustles. The jasmine wafts. The sprinklers spray. The mortuary arrives. The husband is transferred appropriately.

When it's done, the wife finally says she's tired. She's ready to go to bed and gestures down the hall towards the bedroom. I start to say my good-byes when Bruce begins growling. He runs back to the now empty bedroom. The one the husband had been in. Then he changes his path and runs to me. Bruce latches onto my pants leg, pulling at me. *What the heck?*

The wife is mortified. "Stop it," she yells. "Stop that right now. He's not like this. I don't understand." It's the most emotion she's shown all night.

Despite yelling and scolding, Bruce cannot be dissuaded. He continues to growl and grip my pants in his mouth. Seeing no alternative, I finally allow myself to be led into the bedroom, by a geriatric basset hound attach to my leg. The wife follow, apologizing repeatedly.

It's four am now. I'm tired too. *What on earth is wrong with this dog? Did the mortuary miss something?* We saw the husband be transferred and moved. We saw the empty bed. *So what the heck Bruce? What the heck?*

Bruce, the wife, and I enter the bedroom reluctantly. Bruce finally detaches from my leg and starts barking and growling at a dark corner. He then runs back and grabs my slobbery pants leg again. The wife again tells Bruce to "stop it." She's tired and wants to go to bed.

"He's gone," she says to Bruce, "I'm so sorry but he's gone."

The room is dark and my unease is growing despite her reassurances to Bruce.

"Let's turn on a light," I suggest.

The wife flicks the switch.

In the corner, at the edge of the wife's bed, crouches the largest rat I've ever seen outside of a zoo. It hisses and bares its teeth. I move instinctively in front of the wife and the rat goes streaking out of the room. Bruce abandons my pants leg and jumps on the rat's tail biting down. The rat makes a noise somewhere between a scream and squeal. The wife starts screaming, turns white, then sits down on the floor. Still screaming.

I follow the rat-Bruce combo into the living room hoping Bruce has a plan. He does.

Bruce has somehow cornered the rat into a brick fireplace. The rat is trying to climb the back wall. I grab the painting hanging above the fireplace. It's the closest thing at hand. I look at Bruce, big droopy eyes look at me. As I lower the painting over the fireplace opening Bruce releases the giant rat and dashes out. The rat is now trapped behind the painting and isn't pleased. Hissing. Scratching. Screeching. All issue from the fireplace. I hope the canvas holds.

The wife arrives next. She grabs a chair near the fireplace. She pushes it in place over the painting. Then she smiles at Bruce and says, "good boy," while shaking her head.

Good boy Bruce. Good boy.

The wife goes into the kitchen while Bruce sits at my feet, tail wagging. He keeps watch over the hissing, trapped rat. The wife returns with a giant roll of duct tape. We proceed to duct tape the entire chair over the painting and perimeter of the fireplace. While we work the wife turns on an old recording of The Beach Boys. We both sing along to the songs. Bruce occasionally howls.

Bruce eventually falls asleep on the rug. When we're finished we have a giant silver duct tape sculpture covering a still hissing rat. The sun is rising and it still smells like jasmine.

I take the next day off work. As a new nurse I would have shown up for work and kept going. But as a seasoned nurse I decide I've shown up enough for that day. Any days where I'm slobbered on by a basset hound, trap a rat, and create a sculpture from duct tape, all in the wee hours of the morning are days to remember, and to sleep some more. Some days are like that.

41

Spirit and light.

Do I believe in signs? Messages from the beyond or the spiritual realm? This comes up a lot in hospice care. Any end-of-life care really. What happens afterwards? Are there ghosts? Have you seen them? Will people contact you? Do you believe?

I will give you a solid "I don't know, but I'm not ruling anything out" when pressed hard for an answer.

What I do believe in is energy. In spirit and light. I believe the deceased watch out for us when they can. I believe messages may be sent. If we choose to pay attention, we might receive them.

This I have seen. This I believe.

One fine spring day I'm walking home from little league with my son and another boy from our neighborhood. They're both wearing their little league uniforms, first names smartly printed in bright, white block letters on their backs above their numbers. The boys are chattering away about who hit what. Which catches were best. Who slid into which bases.

I have the gear bag. I'm walking a few paces behind. I'm enjoying half-listening to their banter. It's warm with no clouds, a perfect spring afternoon. The traffic through our neighborhood is little to none. We're approaching a street crossing.

A small, maroon two-door car pulls past us, then parks at the crossing. Across the crossing actually, in the middle of the road. A woman climbs out of the driver's seat, the car still running. Dressed head-to-toe in a nice black suit and heels. Tears running down her made-up face. She's partially laughing, somewhat crying, and a-little-bit dancing as she walks around the front of her car, now parked in the middle of the road. The boys are a few paces ahead of me.

They stop walking and bantering. They immediately retreat behind me. I feel my pocket for my phone, ready to call for help if needed. Unstable people usually don't bother me much. I think it's years spent working as a nurse. But this is particularly unusual, and I have the boys with me. The woman approaches, still crying and laughing.

"Bless you. Bless you. Those boys." She points at the boys who are now hiding deeper behind me.

"Those boys in their uniforms. Thank you." She holds her hands together, like she's praying. She looks at me then back at the clear blue sky.

I look up too, hoping to see something that would explain what's happening. Nothing but sky.

She pauses. I look back at her expectantly, my eyebrows raised. Hopeful she knows she isn't making sense. No sense at all. The boys tuck in even closer. The situation doesn't feel dangerous, just odd.

Luckily she gets it. "I came from a funeral," she says, gesturing at the suit.

"My uncle. He's my everything. He rescued me from my momma when I was seven. No daddy. Took me in. Raised me."

She babbles on between cries, incomplete sentences and laughter, "taught me baseball. He was my everything. We would go to games.

Eat peanuts. Keep score." She looks up at the clear blue sky again and shakes her finger. I look too. Still nothing but sky.

"Thank you," she says to the sky again, "thank you." More tears, more dancing. A little hallelujah escapes quietly and hangs in the fresh spring air.

The boys are getting curious. They come out from behind me, a little bit at a time. Baseball?

"He kept me in school. Sent me to college. We always watched baseball," she continues her meandering story.

I briefly wonder, why us? Why here? Why now? I let her carry on though.

"I played softball. I went to college and played softball 'cause of him. He got the cancer. He didn't know until it's too late. He died. My whole family was him. His name was Jonathon Walter. My everything."

She trails off and looks at me, her brown eyes filled with tears. *Oh. I see now. I see.*

I nod my head at her. *I understand. I see.*

She holds her hands up to the sky. "His funeral, it's today. And now this…" She gestures at the two boys again.

She looks at us on the sidewalk, the boys now standing by my sides, not hiding anymore. A few cars have slowly driven around her parked and running car. While the four of us stand on the sidewalk in the sun. I'm aware of the cars driving by slowly, assessing the scene. *We are okay. It's okay. I understand. Spirit and light.*

"I turned off the main road," she says, "and came this way. I didn't know why I was turning. I just did. I live north. But I decided to turn left at the bottom of the hill. That doesn't take me north. I turned by the lake and baseball fields. I turned and then I saw you in the distance and I had a feelin'. A feelin'… Y'all were walking on the sidewalk," she looks at the boys and smiles.

"His name," she pauses and says it again, "his name, it was Jonathon Walter." She looks at the two boys. They smile at her as she smiles at them. I smile too. *Spirit and light.*

"And now I know. It's gonna be okay. He's gone. My uncle's gone. But he's gonna keep lookin' out for me. Thank you." Her hands clasp in prayer. She looks back up at the clear sky, "hallelujah Lord." A deep breath. I nod at her.

Understanding. *Spirit and light.*

As I stand on the street corner. As she looks at me and the boys, I hear Ernesto's children and grandchildren telling me stories. I picture Lydia in a ballgown with one eyebrow missing while she sips tea. I feel the postman's cool, soft hand in mine as he contemplates the difference between living and being alive. I see Kate holding Melissa as she takes her last breath. I recall doing a puzzle late in the afternoon while Abe snoozes and Paulina and I sip dark, bitter coffee. I see Bruce circling my legs and hear the Beach Boys in my memories. I smell jasmine.

It'll be alright. It always is. It may not make sense at the time. It may hurt. It may be the worst pain ever. But it will pass. It'll be different, but it will be alright.

The woman gets back in her car and drives away slowly. We start walking again. The two boys are in front of me and they resume their chattering about baseball. I pick up the gear bag.

The white block letters of their first names on their navy-blue jerseys, "Jonathon" and "Walter," shine in the brilliant spring sunlight.

Thank you universe. Spirit and light. Shine on.

***

If I had to sum up "Blooming" in one word it would be connections. These are nursing and healthcare stories, but I think they are also the stories about being human. I remember these when I think about the most beautiful parts of healthcare. These are mostly stories about people (and a dog and a rat).

There is nursing but there are also tomato plants, turkey basters, puzzles, and jokes. There's tea time, food in a blender, immortality, and beets. These are the gifts that nursing provides once we are comfortable in our skills and competent in our ability to provide care. Find what you love to do in nursing. Go through the painful stages of learning it well. Keep growing as your field changes. And be open to the beautiful moments that happen without warning once you connect with so many other beautiful humans.

Conclusion

" May your choices reflect your hopes,
not your fears. "

- Nelson Mandela

42

Was it worth it?

I'm a nurse. Yet nursing wasn't my calling. It started as a stable paycheck. A way to be independent. It was ever changing and challenging (it still is). It allowed me to help people. To make a difference. And after twenty years, it's become a part of me. Interwoven into the fabric of who I am. I continue to learn and grow in this field of caring. This field that's a mix of art and science and soul and health and caring.

I enjoy helping people. There are scars on my soul that weren't there twenty years ago. Scars that remind me of the people I saved and those I lost. And all those who fell in between.

Scars from when I learned a body and soul are not the same.

Scars from crying in a bathroom when I got too close.

Scars from moments spent with two men and a turkey baster.

There are so many ways to help people that are not nursing. But then I wouldn't really be doing what I've grown to love. Which is helping people when they need it most. Providing care when they might not be able to care for themselves. Connecting with people. I hope I've been able to make a difference, to leave more good in this world. May the balance always shift towards good.

The knowledge required to be a nurse continues to evolve. When I started in nursing I charted on paper flow sheets. I printed ECG strips and taped them onto paper forms. I took verbal orders from doctors and deciphered handwritten orders for all things. That is now in the past. Nursing continues to evolve and change. If you work in nursing, the learning is never done. I embrace this. I love it. It keeps things fresh. If I ever reach a day when I don't want to continue learning, then I'll know it's time to no longer be a nurse. It's time to hang up the stethoscope. To put away the rubber shoes. To leave the world of nursing to a younger, fresher, hungrier generation.

Being a nurse requires a team. When I started out I thought I had to know it all on my own. I thought books had all the answers. I learned quickly that improvisation plays a role in being a good nurse. I ate the cheese crackers. I fixed the headboard. I duct-taped a painting and chair over a fireplace.

I was blessed to be part of a strong team early on. However I didn't have the same experience everywhere I went in my career. I discovered what it felt like to be on the outside as a student and as a nurse practitioner. I learned how it felt to not be wanted, to not fit, to not have a home. I learned how it felt to be shamed in front of my team and have no one come to my defense, including myself. I grew to figure out how to put myself first and leave the jobs where I felt like an outsider. You could make an argument I should have stayed and tried to change the culture from within. But I know my limitations. To stay a nurse, I need a strong team. I cannot be a nurse on my own.

When I started in nursing I didn't know how healthcare and healthy care were different. It took me years to learn the skills and tasks of nursing. I became competent at *the doing*, which opened up doors for *the being*. I found being with patients, connecting with them, was where healthy care existed. In my world healthy care is equivalent to soul care. And soul care is the magic. It's what keeps me coming back.

Soul care is talking with someone about a tomato plant they found at the grocery store.

Soul care is letting someone speak when it takes time and effort. The process might be messy.

Soul care is listening to stories that might meander and wind to find healthcare answers.

Soul care is bearing witness to the love that comes with a lifelong friendship. It's laughing at jokes that make no sense. It's the human part of caring for a human being. It's an excellent reason to become a nurse, to stay a nurse.

So, the question remains, has it been worth it? My answer is yes (mostly).

I'd love to forget some of the more painful experiences but then I wouldn't have gained the knowledge I have from those lessons. They're gifts I wouldn't have received had I done something different with this life. Had I not tried to answer questions I didn't know the answers too. Had I not learned to ask the questions I hate asking, but do anyway, in an attempt to save a life. Had I not been faced with "an other" who helped make my values perfectly clear to me. Each painful experience is a scar *and* a lesson. It's growth, my growth.

There are many stories in this book about death and dying. As I mentioned in one story, we all die. Yet many of us ignore this fact. I wonder if we've missed the point and instead should be focusing on the end. Because it seems to me there's so much living, so much depth, so much value people soak up, simply by knowing there *is* an end. Bearing witness to the end is an unexpected gift of this work in nursing.

Writing this book helped me realize the journey, the trials, the pain, the joy, it's been worth it (mostly). I had no idea how much I'd change. No idea how many things I'd see. How much I'd hurt. How much I'd grow. How much I'd learn. I had no idea how many people I'd meet - so many wonderful, marvelous, surprising, interesting people. How many lives I'd connect with. How many people I'd let go of and miss. I had no idea how much living can be done in the last months, days, or minutes of a life. How much living can be done simply by knowing there is an end. Spirit and light.

I hope this book finds it's way into the hands of nurses just starting out. Or nurses making a change in their career. Or simply nurses wanting to know someone else has faced what they have faced. Nurses who want to know they're not alone. I hope one or two of these stories may save someone the pain I went through. May they learn, be prepared, and possibly navigate things differently. I won't lie, this career in nursing, it's been hard. It's been messy. It's been fun too.

At the end of the day it is painful. It is beautiful. It is worth it, from my view. To be a nurse.

43

My List

Some people love having a list at the end of a book. What was learned? What were the highlights? Give it to me in a few quick bullet points.

I don't know that *this list* is exactly that... but it's an attempt to pull some of the common themes together. And to make a list (for people who like lists).

I like lists, so, here's my list.

What I learned or hope to pass on (in no particular order, because I believe they're all important):

1. Nursing does *not* have to be your calling for you *to do it. And love it.* And have a long, satisfying career in it. But I do recommend finding something you *love* in nursing and doing that (see #9).
2. It's good to have something to discuss with patients that is *not* politics, religion, your family, or anything else that could be polarizing or too personal. Hobbies are good for this - like gardening. Find a hobby.

3. Dentures can come out of the mouth.
4. Listen to your patients. Really listen. Especially if what they're doing doesn't seem to make much sense to you. Listen. There's usually a lesson hidden in there. Listen (see #19).
5. When Hollywood makes a movie it doesn't always follow the book. Life is like Hollywood in this way, it doesn't always follow the book (even the Foundations of Nursing book).
6. Be kind when and where you can be and as often as you can be.
7. Be scrappy. Be innovative. Don't give up.
8. Nurses are people too. We make mistakes, have bad days, and aren't always at our best. Give grace (to yourself and others).
9. Nursing is a huge field of opportunities. Find something in the field of nursing you love to do. Find a team to do it with you. It makes the field of nursing amazing.
10. If you're not sure about something ask questions or clarify. Keep asking until you understand.
11. Be honest.
12. Ask the hard questions when you need to ask them. The really hard questions that might be uncomfortable.
13. Accept there will be many (many) things you do not know. That's part of the fun, learning more things. Be okay with not knowing.
14. Stand up for yourself if you're being treated poorly.
15. Let everyone speak.
16. Stay humble.
17. Keep extra scrubs, socks, and underwear in your car or backpack or locker. Some days are just like that.
18. I've worked with great teams and with not-so-great teams. The work is hard either way, but it's a lot more fun with a team.

19. If you listen to your patients you may receive one of the greatest gifts - hearing their stories, their dreams, their hopes, their fears. They will tell you who they are and it will be beautiful (see #4).

20. Be careful with your heart. Be thoughtful about your boundaries.

21. Respect others' boundaries. Privacy. Walls. Be respectful.

22. Expect to be surprised. Shocked. Delighted. Heartbroken. Changed.

23. Talk about death (as long as it's not prohibited).

24. Ponder the difference between being alive and living. They are not always the same.

25. Embrace any opportunity that comes along to laugh, share jokes, and see the light in this life. And to drink tea (or coffee) and eat cookies.

26. Believe in magic. It exists in the smallest, largest, most ordinary ways. Believe.

27. Trust in something larger and more infinite than yourself.

These resources are provided as a point of reference or in case someone needs help. My only affiliation with these organizations is through ANCC, which I use for my national certification as a nurse practitioner.

ANA Enterprise (Nursing World)

- Improve patient care through supporting both individuals and organizations to advance the nursing profession
- ANA Enterprise exists to give every nurse the best chance of success
- Includes ANA (American Nurses Association) and ANCC (American Nurses Credentialing Center)
- https://www.nursingworld.org/

Crisis Text Line

- Text **HOME** to 741741 from anywhere in the United States, anytime
- The Crisis Text Line is available for any crisis
- A live, trained Crisis Counselor receives the text and responds, all from a secure online platform
- https://www.crisistextline.org/

Hospice Foundation of America

- Educates the public and health care professionals about death, dying and grief
- Funds research about hospice care, supports specific hospice and/or grief initiatives (such as children's grief camps), and financially assists hospice providers in times of disaster
- https://hospicefoundation.org/

National Suicide Prevention Lifeline

- 1-800-273-8255
- Provides 24/7, free and confidential support for people in distress, prevention and crisis resources for you or your loved ones, and best practices for professionals in the United States
- https://suicidepreventionlifeline.org/

SAMHSA (Substance Abuse and Mental Health Services Administration)

- 1-800-662-HELP (4357)
- National Helpline is a free, confidential, 24/7, 365-day-a-year treatment referral and information service (in English and Spanish) for individuals and families facing mental and/or substance use disorders
- https://www.samhsa.gov/find-help/national-helpline

ACKNOWLEDGEMENTS

> " *Unless someone like you cares a whole awful lot,* "
> *nothing is going to get better. It's not.*
> - Dr. Seuss (The Lorax)

To Will, thank you for being with me through the journey of writing and self-publishing this book. Thank you for the gift of time and not letting me delete the early drafts. Thank you for believing I could do this (or at least acting like you did).

To Zachy, thank you for the hugs and encouragement along the way. You made writing a book fun with your smiles and laughter. You are the living embodiment of what it means to care for others. I look forward to seeing where your big compassionate heart takes you in this world.

To Dorothy, our future author and illustrator. I hope your love for writing and creating books continues. I look forward to seeing what you bring to the world in your works. It know it will be wonderful!

To my parents, Steve and Peggy, thank you for instilling a love of books in me at an early age. Thank you for encouraging my passion for reading. It is the reason I am a reader and writer today.

To the Akimbo team, Seth Godin, Kristen Hatcher, the participants in The Creatives Workshop 1 (TCW1), and Writing in Community 3 (WIC3), thank you. This book would not exist in the world without the forum you provided, the community that was created, and the support which carried me through the process.

To Joe T, Monica K, Liz J, Esyltt G, Richard S, thank you for plowing through the early drafts of this book. You provided critical feedback and gave me courage to continue writing.

To Sue H, Anya T, Rachael A, Trent S, David B, Jonathan L, Annie K, Jeannell I, Robin H, Deb M, Salman A, and many more (from TCW1 and WIC3) thank you for the words of encouragement. You may not have known how much your support meant to me at the time. I want you to know, it meant the world.

To the countless people who taught, trained, and took a chance on me becoming the nurse and nurse practitioner I am today, thank you. I hope you know your time and efforts were not wasted. I learned. I grew. I cared. I *still* care. I hope I have made you proud.

Finally, to the patients and families written about here, and for all those who live on in my memories, thank you. While identifying details have all been changed, I hope you know you are the heart and soul of this book. I deeply appreciate the privilege of sharing time with you. The lessons were not always easy. I learned so much becoming the person I am today, in part, due to those lessons, thank you.

With all my gratitude.

ABOUT THE AUTHOR

Rachel Ostrander is a registered nurse and nurse practitioner. She holds a Bachelors in Nursing (Linfield University, School of Nursing) and a Masters in Nursing (University of Washington).

She graduated cum laude from Linfield and was a member of Sigma Theta Tau International. At the University of Washington she was honored to be a recipient of the Comprehensive Geriatric Education Program Traineeship. Her twenty-plus-years nursing career has included positions in telemetry, ICU, cath lab, hospice, anticoagulation, and more. She knows she isn't supposed to pick favorites but if she had to pick one, it would be hospice nursing.

She lives in the Pacific Northwest with her husband and two young kids. When she's not writing you might find her on the trails, camping or swimming in the lake. This is her first published book.